A NATURALISTIC VIEW
OF MAN

Books by George Crile, Jr.

More Than Booty

A Naturalistic View of Man

A
NATURALISTIC
VIEW OF
MAN

The Importance of
Early Training in Learning, Living, and
the Organization of Society

George Crile, Jr., M.D.

THE WORLD PUBLISHING COMPANY
NEW YORK AND CLEVELAND

Published by The World Publishing Company
2231 West 110th Street, Cleveland, Ohio 44102
Published simultaneously in Canada by
Nelson, Foster & Scott Ltd.

First Printing—January, 1969

Manufactured at World Publishing Press,
a division of The World Publishing Company, Cleveland, Ohio.

PRINTED IN THE UNITED STATES OF AMERICA

This book is dedicated
to my collaborator

HELGA SANDBURG

Poetess, novelist,
naturalist, and wife

THE FACE OF THE WATERS

I am told now that the particles in an atom's inner
*   core*
Are so small that no one knows if they are particles
*   at all;*
They no longer seem to take up any space,
Being but bits of energy, existing without form.

As one looks into the space within the atom,
The concepts of form and matter seem to vanish
And in their place is nothing but energy
In an organization we do not understand.

I thought of Genesis, Chapter one, Verse two:
And the earth was without form, and void;
And darkness was upon the face of the deep.
And the Spirit of God moved upon the face of the
    waters.

Now, as in the beginning, there is the concept
Of the unity of the universe;
Mass and energy are interchangeable;
We can no longer separate the spirit from the flesh.
—G. C., J<small>R</small>.

CONTENTS

ix

*To everything there is a season and
a time to every purpose under Heaven.*

—Ecclesiastes 3:1

Introduction

For that which befalleth the sons of men
befalleth beasts; even one thing befalleth
them: as the one dieth, so dieth the other;
yea, they have all one breath; and man
hath no preeminence above the beasts.
—Ecclesiastes 3:19

Recent advances in science and technology have
brought about challenges to many of man's most firmly
fixed definitions and beliefs. Physicians, confronted
with the feasibility of transplanting vital organs from
one person to another, are finding it difficult to define
the point at which death occurs and a donor's vital
organs can justifiably be transplanted into another person. The availability of the contraceptive pill has made
it difficult for theologians to define the point at which
life begins. The possibility of "directed mutation" of
both man and animals is being seriously discussed in
the light of what has been learned about the genetic
code. The exponential growth of populations and its
threat to the earth's ecology has raised the question of
whether people have the right to have as many children

as they want. Traditional ways of rearing infants and young children are being challenged. Conventional methods of teaching are being supplanted by computerized programs of individual instruction. The concept of the book-filled library as the repository of information may soon be supplanted by electronic methods of storing and retrieving knowledge. Freudian beliefs are being rapidly replaced by those of the behavioral psychologists. Not only has it been alleged that "God is dead," but it is also being widely accepted that the mind of man differs from that of other higher animals only in degree and not in any absolute sense. Moreover, the synthesis of the genetic material DNA has broken the last qualitative barrier between what we call life and what we have hitherto thought of as inanimate chemical processes. For the first time in history man is beginning to comprehend the unity of the universe and the interrelationships of the processes that have made it possible for him to exist. These changes in our points of view about life, society, and the place of the individual within society are proceeding so rapidly that tenets and techniques that were taught in school or college are often obsolete by the time the student has been graduated. It is therefore necessary to keep reexamining even our most cherished and certain beliefs.

This book is written from the standpoint of a surgeon with a long-standing interest in biological research, and also from the point of view of an amateur naturalist interested in animal behavior. Its theme is that there is a critical time in the life of each cell, each organ, each animal, each society, and perhaps even in the ecology of the world, at which the organism in question is particularly sensitive to its environment and best able to make an adaptive change. Before or after that time, stimulation may be ineffective. In the words of the Preacher in Ecclesiastes, "There is a time to every purpose."

GEORGE CRILE, JR.
Cleveland, Ohio
1968

CHAPTER ONE

Time, The Determiner of Development

No one can alter the time schedule of the human brain, not even a psychiatrist, or an educator. The built-in biological clock tells the passage of learning aptitudes and the teacher's opportunity.

—Wilder Penfield

Most of a physician's patients do not suffer from physical disease but from symptoms of anxiety and emotional tension. Some of them are benefited by the reassurance of having the cause of the symptoms explained, but in most cases persuasion is of no value. These patients have so little insight and are so unable to view their problems objectively that even psychiatrists are unable to help them.

I had accepted people's emotional disturbances as one of the unalterable facts of life and had stopped thinking much about the subject until about ten years ago when I accidentally encountered a vast new body of information. It happened that I was hunting ducks one day with my late wife Jane, when we came upon some mallards that were too young to fly. We caught them alive and brought them home to the little pool in our fenced-in back yard. It was from observing the ways of these ducks that I became interested in animal behavior and in its relationship to the behavior of human beings. I began to read on the subject and fortunately one of the first books that I encountered was *King Solomon's Ring*, written by the now famous Austrian naturalist Konrad Lorenz. Through it I was introduced to the scientific study of animal behavior that has come to be known as ethology.

The success of medical research is based on the fact that the various organs of animals function in much the same way as the corresponding organs of men. However, when it comes to the function of the brain, as exhibited in behavior, it has often been assumed that there is a fundamental difference between animals and men. This may be a legacy from the concept of the soul, presumed to be unique to the human being. In any event, it is only in the last twenty years that the study of animal behavior has been placed on a scientific basis and its results applied to the problems of human behavior and learning. So rapid has been the progress in this field that it is beginning to seem likely that instinct, learning, emotion, and behavior may be reduced to biological principles. They may be even further resolved into the basic biochemistry of the molecules in which heredity and learning are stored.

The danger in writing about biology is that the subject may be oversimplified and presented as if it were based upon rigid rules rather than broad principles. The process of evolution has been so plastic and so successful in filling every niche of nature with life that it is difficult to classify creatures exactly or generalize on their behavior. Fish may fly, birds may be flightless, certain mammals fly and others live largely under water; some reptiles give birth to living young; and the platypus, a mammal, lays eggs. Yet there are basic principles that apply to the development and behavior of all.

Most people know little about the factors that affect physical development or of the instincts that are innate in man and animals and they know even less of the way experiences or deprivations, encountered early in life, alter instincts and affect subsequent behavior. Few people have much knowledge of the way the human body develops or the mind learns. This is true also of most physicians, for when they were in medical school a decade or more ago, little was known of these subjects. Yet today, as a result of the astonishing progress in the fields of chemistry, biology, embryology, psychology, ethology, and sociology, man is at last able to catch a glimpse into the nature of himself. This glimpse reveals not only the chemical mechanisms of life, but also the importance of the timetable of development that is contained within the fertilized egg cell.

In the first days of the microscope, it was reported by

researchers that a *homunculus*, a tiny creature with the form of a man, was seen within each human sperm cell. Drawings of the little man appeared in the scientific books of the time. Now it seems that this fantastic concept has almost been surpassed by the reality, for within a structure so small as to be invisible to the naked eye, there exists the chemically coded image of the man. The genes of the cell from which every living creature develops contain the chemical blueprints for building that individual, the sequence and timing of its development, and the starting and stopping of every future cell's growth. Because the biological processes that regulate the growth and development of cells are similar to those that control the growth and development of multicellular animals, and because they are also analogous to the principles that direct the growth and organization of societies, it is worth knowing a little of the basic mechanism by which a cell stores and transmits the information that is necessary for its survival.

Within the nucleus of one mammalian cell is a thread of DNA (deoxyribonucleic acid) which would extend fifty meters, it has been estimated, if stretched full length. This strand of DNA is tightly wound in a spiral as though onto a spool and is so thin that it makes over four billion turns. Within each atom-sized segment of the thread of DNA is a chemically coded message bearing a specific instruction for the future development of some part of the creature. Millions of these coded messages are included in the strand and together compose the genes, each with a fixed location and in charge of a specific feature of development. It is the sum of this coded information that constitutes the image of the future individual.

Growth is the wellspring of life. From the descendants of a single cell, it produces the fully developed plant or animal, then sustains it by constant replacement of injured or dead cells. Scientists have answered some questions about growth; many more remain a mystery. Certain tissues of certain plants appear to grow indefinitely. The cambium layers of the giant sequoias have been growing for four thousand years. Other tissues, such as the pith and bark, cease growing. No matter how much food and attention a carrot root or potato receives, after it has reached a certain size it will not grow any more. It is thought that the controlling signal in these cases is the environment in which each cell is placed as time passes.

If a single-cell amoeba is put into a culture medium and given adequate food and oxygen, it will divide again and again until the bottom of the flask is so covered with amoebas that they touch one another. Then they stop dividing. Their growth was controlled by the contact of the one-celled creatures with each other. If they are shaken up so that they lose contact with one another, the amoebas will again begin to divide. It is likely that the growth of all plants and animals is controlled by similar contact mechanisms as well as by the accumulation, within the system, of chemicals that inhibit further growth.

For a long time it was believed that only the egg cell of a plant or animal was capable of properly reproducing it. Now it seems that every cell within every creature's body contains in its genes a full set of chemical blueprints and has the potential for recreating the individual. This was demonstrated through an experiment with a carrot made by a tissue culturist in France in 1937. Ordinarily in the first year of life, a carrot makes a fleshy root and a small leafy growth. In the second year, it makes a tall seed stalk where the stamen fertilizes the ovule and the seeds develop, after which the plant loses its vigor and dies. When a cell was taken from a nongrowing region of the carrot root and placed in a special nutrient fluid, it was found that it grew astonishingly fast and formed a mass of fluffy cells, bearing no resemblance to a carrot. This mass of cells is still alive after three decades. Within the last fifteen years, single cells have been successfully removed from it and transplanted into a suitable medium and then into vermiculite and soil. Eventually each cell formed a mature carrot with normal root, stalk, flowers and seeds. These carrots withered and died within their usual two-year course of life. Like Adam, when he ate from the tree of knowledge, the cell taken from the formless mass traded its immortality for the opportunity to attain its full genetic potential. Perhaps if we master the techniques of tissue culture, it will someday be possible to remove a single cell from a person and have it grow into a replica of himself.

The first time the single cell of a human embryo

divides, the thread of DNA replicates itself perfectly, so that the two resulting cells are identical. If they are separated at this stage they give rise to identical twins. When the two cells stay together, however, they begin to have an effect upon one other. Differences begin to appear. When they divide again, each of the cells that are produced, although still having identical genes, once again become different from the other. As these changes proceed, each type of cell begins to develop a characteristic chemical composition. This process is termed *differentiation*. It shapes not only the organs of the body, but the brain as well, and in this way determines, to a large extent, what the individual's behavior will be.

Differentiation is nature's most dramatic example of the effect of environment on development and of the ability of organisms to mold one another's destiny. This principle is important in the understanding of mankind, because it applies not only to the development of individual cells within a human body, but also to the development of individual people within societies. If differentiation is to proceed normally, its timing must be perfect. Stimuli are ineffective if they come too early or too late.

An explanation of the process of differentiation is the "feedback theory," which has recently been successfully demonstrated by biochemists. Feedback is the term used by electrical engineers to describe a mechanism in which part of a systemic output is fed back into the system in order to control its output. This may be understood by considering what takes place in a colony of bees or ants.

Every unspecialized larva of an ant or bee is capable of developing into a specialized member of the colony, such as the queen or a soldier. Only if a lack occurs within one of the castes and there is a gap that needs to be filled will the specialized development take place. When the specialized places are filled, the development of the larva is inhibited because of feedback of chemical substances which are produced by the specialized caste. Within a developing embryo chemical reactions may be similarly inhibited by minute quantities of cellular products. As an embryo develops, there are many pathways open to individual cells, but they become fewer and fewer as the specialized parts of the embryo take shape and each begins to produce its characteristic chemicals.

Experiments to demonstrate the feedback principle were done by scientists at the University of Illinois. Frog eggs were cultivated in pieces of adult frog's brain, heart, or blood. Some of the embryos which had been cultured with adult brain developed to the stage in which brain would be expected, but none formed; in others the brain developed late or abnormally. In the group cultured with adult heart tissue, a heart failed to develop. Those grown in diluted adult blood did not produce blood on time. In another set of experiments at Johns Hopkins University, the extract of an adult frog was injected into frog eggs. The eggs divided and grew normally for a while and then stopped. They had not died; they simply remained in a state of suspended animation. As far as the embryonic frogs were concerned, the chemicals of a mature frog were already present so there was no need for further growth.

It is a familiar phenomenon that if a leaf is removed from certain house plants and put in water, it will grow roots from the base of the stem. If the growing tip of a sapling is removed, it will be replaced by a new tip on a branch below. In all of these cases, the presence of a specialized part discourages the development of a similar part; the removal of a specialized part causes other cells to take its place and perform its function.

The operation of complex chemical systems of inhibition in a developing embryo determines the tissues and organs that will develop, as well as their location. This process probably involves either the suppression of a function of a gene or the release of the function of a gene from suppression. Although the blueprints in the genes of every cell are identical, each cell uses only a minute part of them to build its particular destiny. The rest of the genes are suppressed by feedback from other cells. In this respect the cell resembles a human being who is born with the potential of specializing in any of a number of lines—plumber, lawyer, physicist, soldier. What he will do usually depends more on what openings and opportunities are available in his society than on his potential at birth.

Throughout all observations on growth and development runs the theme that time is a crucial factor. At critical periods in the fetal life of a baby, hormones may effect permanent changes in its anatomy. An excess of the hormone progesterone may result in the masculinization of female babies. If the brain of a fetus is not receiving an adequate amount of thyroid hormone, cretinism may result. Chemicals foreign to the body, given at critical periods, can be disastrous, as for example, the deformed babies that resulted when the sleeping pill Thalidomide was taken by the mothers. It is only for a brief period of a few days, when the limb buds are developing, that Thalidomide produces its characteristic deformity. If hormones or chemicals are administered outside of the critical time, they may have no significant effect. Conversely, if the necessary hormone or chemical is not present at the right time, no later treatment will remedy the deficiency.

In a growing organism the most severe deficits and deformities occur as a result of deprivations or exposures encountered early in the course of development. These tend to be irreversible, for there is no way to turn back the flow of time. The principle that the appropriate stimulus must occur at the proper time applies to the development of the mind as well as the body. If an individual is to grow up with emotional stability and if he is to achieve his measure of contentment, the experiences of infancy and childhood are of the utmost importance.

The brain of a baby at birth is only partly developed, and weighs less than a quarter as much as an adult's brain. Its contour is like that of the lower animals'. The temporal lobes, which are enormous in the adult human in comparison with other animals, are largely missing. The baby's brain remains in this embryonic stage for about two years. What happens to the brain from birth into early childhood, therefore, is as important to the development of the mind as was what happened before birth to the development of the body. The measure of love the child receives, the types of training and education and the time when they take place, will determine the characteristics of the future man.

Since the first caveman brought in the first wolf pup, it has been known that very young animals are more easily tamed than old ones. It was not, however, until thirty years ago, when the Austrian naturalist Konrad Lorenz coined the term *imprintation* that the phenomenon began to be studied by scientists. Lorenz, working with newly hatched goslings and ducklings, found that they became imprinted in the brief period between the twelfth and forty-eighth hour after hatching. During this time they adopted as their foster mother, and became permanently attached to, whatever creature or thing they were with at that time. They accepted the foster mother and all like it as one of their own species. Lorenz discovered that forty-eight hours or more after hatching, it became progressively more difficult to imprint the babies. After a week it was impossible. The creatures could no longer identify themselves with a foster mother.

Imprintation occurs in mammals as well as birds. At

first, when the babies are helpless and have neither fear of danger nor the ability to avoid it, they are immune to imprintation. The period in which the baby is imprintable occurs at the time when it first becomes capable of following a mother or escaping an enemy. This is just before the time at which fear of strangers develops. Lambs and fawns, born, like ducklings, fully developed and capable of following, are imprintable from the moment of birth. Raccoons or foxes, born helpless, as are most baby birds, do not become imprintable until they are able to move about and follow their mothers.

Margaret and Harry Harlow, working with primates, showed that there is a critical period in which, if the baby monkey is not cared for by a monkey mother, or does not at least play with young monkeys of its own age, the course of its life is irrevocably changed. It never learns to make a satisfactory social or sexual adjustment. Even an innate behavior pattern, such as grooming, if prevented too long from being expressed, begins to regress. Once the critical time for its development is past, it is impossible to elicit the action again. Perhaps the irreversible emotional instability that affects so many people has its origin in deprivations experienced early in childhood, for there seems to be no fundamental qualitative difference between the brains of human beings and those of other higher animals.

The only skills that man does not share with some other animal appear to be the symbolism of language and the ability to use complex tools. Jackdaws, for example, are able to discriminate numbers up to seven. This prelinguistic number sense is equal to a human's, for if a man does not use the symbols with which he can count, he can seldom estimate the number, at a glance, of more than seven objects at a time.

The use of tools is not limited to man. Sea otters use rocks to break open seashells, which they hold upon their bellies and pound while floating on their backs. The higher apes too are able to use simple tools, and at times behave in ways that are reminiscent of our own. A captive female chimpanzee not only had a pet kitten, but also played with dolls which she treated maternally.

Animals possess in a degree all of the qualities of human beings. They are capable of extraordinary love. They have a strong sense of curiosity. They like to play. There are countless tales of their demonstrations of altruism. Recent studies of the killer whale and the porpoise suggest that they employ the symbolism of language, communicating with a system of clicks and squeaks. The porpoise's brain, in relation to its body weight, is larger than that of a man and contains more cells. It is possible that it is capable of performing feats of communication, symbolism, and learning of which earthbound man is quite unaware.

Observations made on animals emphasize the irreversibility of early experience and the importance of timing in the process of learning. In regard to man, this implies that the mood of a lifetime is set in the forgotten events of childhood. The theme is not a new one. Years ago Freud wrote, "We must assume or we may convince ourselves through psychological observations on others, that the very impressions which we have forgotten have nevertheless left the deepest traces on our psychic life and acted as determinants for our whole future development."

CHAPTER TWO

Instinct and Memory

It will be universally admitted that instincts are as important as corporeal structures for the welfare of each species under its present conditions of life.
—Charles Darwin: *Origin of Species*

After Jane and I caught the young ducks and put them on our pond, we introduced a number of birds and animals into the back yard and spent much of our spare time in studying their behavior. Then Jane died and later I married Helga Sandburg, a writer and a naturalist who also had a keen interest in all living things.

In our first summer together Helga and I built a one-room cabin, thirty feet square, in the forest on our country place twenty-five miles east of Cleveland. We call it the Unicorn's Lair, and go there weekends to visit the variety of tame creatures that we moved from the townhouse yard and now keep in a fenced-in acre around the cabin.

One day the baby pheasants, the pet crow, and the

guinea fowl outside the door of the Unicorn's Lair cried out suddenly in alarm. Then they cowered, motionless, as a Cooper's hawk swooped down over the garden and winged away. None of the birds had ever seen a hawk before. Their reaction to it was instinctive.

An instinct is an inherited, built-in pattern of behavior. Birds that have never seen a hawk cower or take cover when a hawk flies by or even when an object shaped like a hawk is passed over them. Baby opossums, as soon as born, go unerringly to their mothers' pouches and find the teats. As soon as a tiny sea turtle hatches, it digs its way up out of the sand and heads straight for the sea. A human baby does not have to be taught to suck or even to walk.

As a bird or animal matures in its natural habitat, its instinctive behavior develops as precisely as does the color of its coat or the arrangement of its plumage. Because of this, it is sometimes hard to tell whether a pattern of behavior has been learned from a parent or is the result of an instinct that developed gradually. This confusion causes people to say that a bird is "learning" to fly, which is not true. For example, when pigeons are released after being reared in narrow tubes which prevent them from using their wings, they will fly as well as others that were left free to practice flight. The instinctive behavior pattern of flight in the young pigeons matures at a steady rate, independent of practice. The same principle seems to apply to man, for it was found that Hopi Indian babies, strapped all day into cradle boards in their mothers' backs, were able to walk at the same age as babies left free to walk when they pleased.

Athough instinctive behavior develops spontaneously as an animal matures, it can be either modified or suppressed. If a baby goat is taken from its mother at birth and its mouth is pushed into a pan of warm milk, it will at once suck up the milk. When this pattern of behavior is established, the kid will disregard its mother's teats. On the other hand, if it is once allowed to suckle from her, the instinct becomes so firmly set that it is difficult to teach the kid to drink from a pan. Again, if an adult wood duck is pinioned after it is mature and has learned to fly it will always, when chased, persist in trying to fly, tumbling awkwardly and falling. However, if it is pinioned early in life, before flight has developed, this instinct to fly will have been suppressed and the bird will try to escape by running away.

The behavior patterns of insects, like spiders, are directed almost entirely by instincts and are innate in their genes. In the higher animals, however, and especially in man, it is difficult and often impossible to say what is innate and what had been learned. Thus, the instinctive behavior of infants and children can be vastly modified or suppressed by training. If the Hopi Indians had not allowed their children to walk when it was time to, they might have grown up like children in certain orphanages, where they were confined to cribs and were unable to walk even at four years of age.

In higher animals, experiences continually alter

behavior, for they have a large part of their brains set aside for the storage of memories. Here the results of trial and error are reinforced by memories of reward and are suppressed by those of punishment. In this way the animal acquires new patterns of behavior, and adapts to its environment.

There is also in the brain an innate guiding mechanism, similar to an instinct, by means of which a rabbit is directed to explore its environment for green things to eat and a fox to explore it for rabbits to eat. Due to the mechanism, a mole burrows underground, and a vulture seeks high places from which to observe the terrain beneath it. The behavior traits which have been acquired by a species and transmitted through heredity, constantly blend in this way with the information the individual obtains through its own experience.

Until the innate qualities which compose the primary programming of a creature's brain are understood, it is impossible to comprehend either its process of learning or its capabilities. Wood ducks nest in a hollow tree and the babies, unable to see in the dark, are programmed to follow the mother's high-pitched chirp when she leaves the nest. A mallard, on the contrary, nests in the open and her ducklings are programmed to follow her by sight. If one is not aware of this and gives a setting of wood duck eggs to a mallard to incubate, disaster ensues. When the eggs hatch, the mallard leaves her nest, confident that the babies will follow. When they don't, she quacks loudly, but the wood ducklings, programmed for chirps, are unable to follow by sight, scatter, and soon are lost.

A turkey hen is programmed to the sound of the chicks' peeping and doesn't recognize her babies by sight. If an object which peeps like a chick is offered to a turkey hen hatching a brood, she will accept it as her own. If anything approaches her nest which doesn't peep like a chick, she will kill it. If the hen is rendered deaf, she will destroy her own chicks. It is odd that we know much more about the programming of certain domestic animals than we do about that of human beings.

The instinctive part of programming is transmitted by the genes in the same way as are inherited physical characteristics. However, before an innate pattern of behavior can be transmitted it must be acquired by a species. How this happens and how a species adapts to its environment is explained by the neo-Darwinian concept of evolution. This combines Darwin's concept of natural selection and Mendel's concept of the gene.

Darwin's theory of survival of the fittest explains how a maladapted mutation, such as a bird's failure to develop a beak, results in the bird's death before it can transmit the mutant gene to descendants. This does not explain, however, how a mutation of little or no survival value, such as the development of a longer beak in a bird already well adapted, could give the mutant bird and its descendants any advantage in respect to survival. Nor does it take stock of the fact that creatures are constantly learning new skills. An example is the great tits of England learning to open milk bottles. Once a new skill is learned by a species, the individuals that are best adapted to practice it will have the best chance of survival. Thus, as Arthur Koestler has said, when a species discovers a new way to exploit its environment, it directs, to some extent, the course of its own evolution.

According to neo-Darwinian theory, the mutation must be considered not only in relation to the survival of an individual but in terms of the survival of a gene. Any mutant gene of advantage or even of neutral survival value is transmitted by the mutant animal's sexual activity into the genetic pool of the species. Throughout the centuries, the genetic pool of each species accumulates a great number of mutant genes which are available to draw upon in case of an adverse environmental change. They are the species' insurance for future survival. If the environment alters so that individuals with normal characteristics of the species are at a disadvantage they will die. Those carrying the mutant genes will interbreed and give rise to a new mutant species which will survive in the new environment. An example is the peacock, whose plumage may not have helped it to survive in the jungle, but did not interfere with survival. Ultimately, when man invaded the jungle and changed the environment, the peacock's beauty impelled man to domesticate it. In this way the species was preserved by a trait that in the original environment had no survival value.

The process of evolution may be likened to trial-and-error learning conducted on a species level. The mutations are the trials. The elimination of a mutant gene through the death of its bearer is the punishment for error. Its perpetuation in the genetic pool is the reward for success. The instinctive parts of human behavior developed through evolution are, therefore, the sum of what the genes of mankind have learned about their environment.

The human being, of all the animals except perhaps the large sea mammals, has the greatest proportion of his brain available for learning. However, instinct, as we have seen, plays a large part in determining what a creature will learn. Man's racial heritage, as expressed in his instincts, may be as immutable as are those of many other animals, if in early life they are reinforced by experience. In an era in which man has made so many violent changes in his natural environment, the question rises as to whether the innate part of his being can adapt. In order to remain in harmony with his environment, man may have to change it back into a more natural one, or else attempt to rear his children, from the earliest age, by special measures so they will be able to adapt to their unnatural surroundings.

It is difficult to change the instinctive reactions that are stored in the primitive part of the brain or programmed in early life, during the period of childhood amnesia. This is not true of the information stored in the other part, which is concerned with memories which an individual acquires later in life. The reaction to a stimulus in the latter area may change as additional information is received. But in the primitive area, so intimately connected with hate, fear, love, and sense of values, the reinforcement of instincts by early experience results in the establishment of patterns of behavior that are most difficult to change.

The cooperation of the two areas, one concerned with racial and the other with individual learning, is thought to be made possible by the storage of all memories both racial and personal in RNA (ribonucleic acid), in which the brain cells and the nervous system are rich. The genes of the cells in the brain are made of DNA (deoxyribonucleic acid). The DNA is the template or mold on which RNA, in mirror image, is cast. When this happens, the RNA leaves the DNA of the nucleus and migrates to the cytoplasm of the cell. It has been called *messenger RNA* because it carries the information it acquired from the DNA.

RNA is the template or mold on which the proteins of the cells are cast. The type of protein, and thus the type of cell which will develop, is determined by the conformation of the molecules of RNA. It is thought that it is not only the inherited patterns of the individual's instinctive behavior that are coded in the molecules of RNA, but also the learning which the individual acquires. Although the evidence is not complete, RNA is beginning to be termed *the molecule of memory*.

One of the pioneers in the molecular theory of

memory is Dr. James V. McConnell, of the Mental Health Research Institute at the University of Michigan. In his laboratory, RNA was taken from the brains of trained rats and injected into the fluid around the brains of untrained ones. The evidence appears to show that part of the learning was transferred.

McConnell and others in the field believe that it is too early to say definitely that RNA is *the molecule of memory* but most of them agree that it is involved in the storage of memories. Perhaps it is only one part of a chain of processes which, taken all together, function to store memories. Incoming signals from sensory organs may be coded by chemical changes in the RNA and then transmitted elsewhere.

Regardless of the exact process by which it is accomplished, the nature of long-term memory seems to be chemical. This has been demonstrated in experiments with flatworms in which the tiny creatures were trained to run mazes. When RNA was extracted from the bodies of the trained flatworms and injected into untrained ones, some of the learning seemed to be transferred. Other experiments also support the concept of the chemical nature of memory. When an animal was given an enzyme which interfered with the formation of new RNA, it did not affect performance of previously learned acts but blocked ability to learn anything new. When rats were given the chemical magnesium pemoline, which increases the production of RNA in the brain, they were able to learn four or five times faster than before. It has been suggested that the memory of aged humans improves after oral administration of this chemical. However, these experiments have not yet been satisfactorily confirmed.

Even the lowliest creatures are able to adapt and remember. Bacteria become resistant to the presence of penicillin in their culture medium if it is added in gradually increasing concentrations. They accomplish this through the survival of mutant bacteria that bear the trait of resistance. These transfer to nonresistant bacteria, through hairlike projections of tissue, a genetic material, probably RNA, which carries information about how to build resistance to the antibiotic. This enables the "educated" ones to transmit the resistance not only to their descendants but also to their naive brothers.

Lymphocytes, the cells which produce many of the immune reactions of the body, are able upon contact with a foreign protein to make a specific antibody to neutralize that protein. Once this ability has been acquired by the lymphocyte, it is not forgotten. The information is stored in its genetic code and transmitted to its descendants and perhaps to other lymphocytes. If the daughter cells are exposed to the same foreign protein, they will make the identical antibody that the original cell made. The success of vaccination is dependent upon this process.

The theory that information is coded and stored in RNA explains much of how memory is transferred from cell to cell and how instincts are transmitted from one creature to its descendants. It explains also how it is possible for mankind's racial wisdom, transmitted as instincts, stored in the genes, to blend so smoothly with the knowledge the individual acquires from his environment.

The success or failure of the transfer of information depends to a large degree on the sequence and timing of experiences. There is a specific time at which each type of learning can most effectively be blended with instincts into the formation of the personality. If the timetable is not followed, it may be difficult to combine the chemically coded instincts and memories into a well-adapted pattern of behavior. In this connection it is clear that the first years of life are of vital importance, for during that period instincts are irreversibly reinforced or permanently obliterated.

CHAPTER THREE

Imprintation and Associative Learning

Give me a child for seven years, and he is mine forever.

—Old Saying

Our blue jay, Ivan, whom we reared from a nestling, learned early from Helga to whistle the first few bars of "The Star-Spangled Banner." Now mature, Ivan still whistles those notes: he never screams the wild jay call. This is because the time when birds learn their songs coincides with the period in which they are imprintable. The same timetable may apply to man and his language, for it is only in the early years that most children can learn to speak a foreign tongue without an accent. It is then also that man can most readily develop an ear for music. In Japan, the famous Suzuki Institute for violinists starts its students in an intensive course of ear-training at the age of three, when the children have been found to be most imprintable.

If man, like all other mammals, is indeed subject to imprintation, then each child travels through time as if on a one-way street. When a period in which the brain is adapted to acquire a certain type of learning passes without receiving the appropriate stimulus, the moment cannot be recaptured. The child cannot turn back; he must travel forward on the road to which he has been committed.

It is probable that in mankind, the crucial period which corresponds to imprintation in the lower creatures encompasses the time of childhood amnesia. This period lasts from birth to the age of four or five, for few people have conscious memories of even dramatic experiences occurring during that time. The phenomenon of childhood amnesia may be due to the fact that at birth and in the early years a child's brain is different from an adult's, the temporal cortex being still in the process of development.

Although at birth the higher centers of the baby's brain are undeveloped, experiences are continually being recorded in the lower centers. Patterns of behavior are being established, as firm as those left in animals by imprintation. This process blends indiscernibly into the later process of associative learning. Yet these two kinds of learning are fundamentally dissimilar.

One of the obvious differences between the two is that a creature is imprintable only in its youth, whereas the ability to learn by association persists through life.

In animals, imprintation may result in patterns of behavior that are as rigid and difficult to change as those that are inherited as instincts; whereas habits acquired later in life are much easier to alter. It seems that imprintation operates to insure *consciousness of species.* The baby animal is learning to know what creature it will regard, thereafter, as its own kind. The information acquired during this period often produces irreversible changes in behavior and has a profound influence on later life. An example is the sexual response of our hand-reared fallow deer who was brought up with a huge dog, Gustav. The doe rejects buck deer, and when in season displays to Gustav, grooms him, and on several occasions has even tried to mount him, as does, in season, will often do to one another.

Imprintation is reinforced by punishment. If a duckling is pecked at as it follows its mother, or if a baby animal must spend a great deal of effort in climbing over rough terrain in following an adopted parent, the imprintation is stronger than if the creature were not so treated. The reverse is true of associative learning, in which punishment deters.

During the critical period of imprintation, the first experience encountered is the one most firmly established. In learning by association, the most recent experience is apt to be the best remembered. When meprobamate, a tranquilizing drug thought to act on the more primitive part of the brain, is given to ducklings, they will learn to solve problems as fast as untreated ones, but they cannot be imprinted. This suggests that there is a fundamental difference between the brain mechanisms involved in imprintation and associative learning.

The general arrangement and function of the brain is similar in man and animals, but there are quantitative differences. The cerebral cortex, commonly called the gray matter, is the outer cellular layer of the brain. This is the *new* brain, which becomes increasingly larger as one ascends the phylogenetic scale from fish to man.

Each sensory organ of the body of both animals and man is connected with a corresponding area in the cerebral cortex. These have been called projection areas, for they are like screens on which images of the environment are projected. In the cerebral cortex also are motor areas, each of which stimulates and coordinates the muscular activity of a certain part of the body.

Although the parts of the brain that have to do with sensation or motion are much alike in man and other animals, the temporal lobes of the human brain are uniquely large. In the first two years these two lobes, almost absent at birth, grow rapidly, room for this growth being provided by the ununited gaps between the bones of the skull that form the so-called soft spot.

The temporal cortex is not committed, as is the rest of the cortex, to fixed functions, such as recording sensations or activating muscles. It is destined to be used for communication, perception, and for the recall of experiences. Dr. Wilder Penfield, professor of neurosurgery at McGill University, has called this area *the uncommitted cortex.* Working with patients with epilepsy or brain injuries, Dr. Penfield made brain maps. These showed that about one-quarter of the cortex of the left temporal lobe is used by a child for language and becomes his speech center. It is concerned with memory and the use of words. The remaining three-quarters is used for recording memories of experiences and interpreting them in the light of present events. It is called the interpretive cortex.

The nerve cells and their connections in the brain are organized as a hierarchy, with the interpretive cortex of the temporal lobe at the summit. In the course of operations on his epileptic patients, who were conscious but kept from pain by local anesthesia, Penfield searched for the focus from which their seizures arose by stimulating various parts of the cortex with a weak electric current. Stimulation of the interpretive part of the temporal cortex evoked vivid memories of the past and illusions about the present, but if a part lower in the brain's hierarchy, such as the visual center, was stimulated, the response was not a visual memory, but merely a flash of light. If a motor center was touched the response was not a coordinated action, but a twitch of a muscle.

Underlying the cortex is white matter made up of the branching connections of nerve cells. These are capable of transmitting electric currents which go from the cortex into the *old* brain or lead to the eyes and ears or pass through the spinal cord to the muscles and skin. As the child begins to learn, the electric currents move through the cortex and the underlying brain. Every time a track is made, it aids the passage of later currents. The initial ones, formed during the period of childhood amnesia, are like paths through a meadow, which once established are always used.

The experiences of early childhood are firmly recorded in the lower centers of the *old* brain and exert a profound effect on subsequent behavior. However, they are isolated and inviolable. There is no way for them to become connected with the interpretive cortex, which has not yet developed, and hence they can never be either retrieved as memories or altered by comparisons with subsequent experienences. They are like the patterns of behavior that are inherited as instincts, or are acquired as a result of imprintation.

The indelible record of early experiences, in combination with the fixed traits of innate behavior, determine the basic programming of a child's brain upon which will be superimposed all later learning. If a child does not receive adequate attention and richness of social experience in early life the results are apt to be irreversible. No amount of subsequent training can fully compensate for the error. Nature relies heavily on the behavior of the mother toward the newborn in its first years of life.

Penfield, in his brain maps, was able to locate precisely the center in the brain concerned with speech and communication. He found that although the center which controls the muscles of the mouth is separate from the one which controls the muscles of the hand, that part of their function which is related to the communication has a common center in the brain. This speech or communication center is responsible for all activities in the field of communication. If it is damaged, the ability to communicate is lost. The mouth can still eat, but it cannot speak. The hand can be used for purposes such as bringing the spoon to the mouth, but it cannot write or beckon.

If the speech center of a child is destroyed by an injury to the dominant, usually the left, temporal cortex the child may recover after a year or so and learn to speak again, using the still uncommitted cortex of the right or non-dominant side. However, if an adult's speech center is severely injured, the originally uncommitted cortex of the opposite side has been taken over for other purposes and the speech center can never be transferred to that side of the brain. By the time a child has grown up, the temporal cortex of the other side is too full of memories and associations to be used for speech.

The facility for learning language, like the ability to recover from injury, is dependent on the age of the person. The first language is set by the age of four or five. If a child has learned a second tongue at the same time, both of them will be well established. The two languages can be likened to different sensory perceptions, such as touch and sight. They amplify each other. Rather than confusing the accuracy of a final impression, they make it more precise. Penfield says there is a kind of switch that enables a child to make an effortless change from one language to another as required. He reared his own children bilingually, speaking German in the nursery with their governess who could speak nothing else, and French with their parents and in their Montreal schoolroom.

There are two ways of learning languages: direct and indirect. Penfield calls the first the "mother's method," for the language is not taught but learned as a product of other pursuits. The indirect method is the schoolteaching way in which the acquiring of the language is an end in itself. The child who learns by the direct method speaks with the exact accent of the teacher, an achievement impossible for most adults. Also he associates the word directly with the action or object, and does not need to translate it. Obviously this method is the most effective. If bilingual and multilingual households could have "upstairs" and "downstairs" or "kitchen" and "living room" languages, the children of the family would absorb them readily.

The concept is not new. Four centuries ago Montaigne, in an essay on education, said, "I would have a lad sent abroad very young in those neighboring nations whose language is most different from our own, and to which, if it not be formed betimes, the Tongue cannot bend." Montaigne, who devoted much of his life to the study of Latin classics and whose writings are firmly based on those of the Roman and Greek philosophers, was reared by a Latin tutor. Until the age of six he spoke nothing but Latin either with tutor or family.

At the Berlitz School of Languages in Washington, D.C., André Pacatte, then the director, developed a method of language teaching called "T.I.," or Total Immersion. This is an attempt to simulate the "mother's method" of learning. The student is taught continuously all day and most of the night, for more than a week, with little time for sleep. No word of the student's native language is ever used. It is like a brainwashing, one series of teachers replacing another and running down the resistance of the pupil methodically. After a course of Total Immersion, Pacatte reports that short periods of practice will hold this student far ahead of one who has had the same number of hours of teaching spread over a month or more.

The reason that a second language is best learned at the time the first language is being acquired is because the brain at that time is a blank record, programmed to record languages. Later the fixation of the patterns or schema of the first language interferes with the learning of the second. The same is true of learning a skill, like roller skating. Thirty years ago Myrtle McGraw quickly trained an eleven-month-old baby to roller skate at the same time the child was learning to walk. His twin, who was not given lessons until he was twenty-two months old, was slow in learning because the schema of walking had been established and suppressed the ability to learn to skate. Psychologists refer to the principle of presenting the child with a learning problem at exactly the period in which he is ready for it as "matching." Teachers have not yet begun to explore its full potential. Although no one remembers the experiences of learning to speak, walk, read, write, or even of learning to ride a bicycle early in life, no one forgets how to do what he learned at that period. In a similar way it would seem that tastes and desires, prejudices and fears, are molded by environmental exposures and by experiences which occur too early to be consciously recalled. It is the period in which character and personality are formed.

Once when I was driving through the countryside of Ireland, I stopped to pick up a girl of about eight, who was thumbing a ride. She was as pretty and blue-eyed as any Irish girl, but she did not have an Irish tongue. Withdrawn, she sat hunched in the far side of the seat and stared out of the window, refusing to talk. When she asked to be let out and I stopped the car, she stretched out her hand and demanded a penny. I asked why I should pay for giving her a ride. "I will curse you if you don't," she said. "I am a Gypsy!" Although the genes of the swarthy central European wanderers had been bleached out by centuries of intermingling with Nordic blood, in behavior, instilled from infancy, the little girl was as much a Gypsy as her Romany ancestors.

When mallard ducks who have been reared in incubators are given a choice between nesting on the ground or in boxes, they will choose the boxes, whereas the ones reared in the wild will always pick a nesting spot on the ground. Men from the Mediterranean islands, where there is no living to be made from the exhausted stony soil, leave their homes to work abroad until they have amassed enough money to return to their places of origin to retire and die. Wood ducks, reared in our back-yard pond in Cleveland Heights, fly south in winter and return in spring to the same tiny pond. A pair of wing-clipped Canada geese, hand-reared and released seventy-five years ago on a lake near our house in the country, now have descendants by the hundreds which return to mate in this area of Ohio, where never before in the memory of residents had a Canada goose remained to raise her young.

The influences of the surroundings of early life are undeniable. In the human being, the decor of the child's home, the associations with people and animals, the music heard, the attitudes observed, the ideas discussed, all put their mark on the future man as firmly as physical qualities such as red hair and brown eyes, which the child inherits through the genes.

CHAPTER FOUR

The Motivation of Learning

We cannot know the consequences of suf-focating a spontaneous action *at the time when the child is just beginning to be active; perhaps we suffocate* life itself.
—Madame Montessori

In the garden of the Unicorn's Lair we have, among other creatures, four who were reared together: two deer, a Canada goose, and a rabbit. The goose and the rabbit are accustomed to the deer and follow them about as they graze, or eat with their heads beside them as they move across the garden. In the early morning and again in the evening, the animals play a game. One deer stands erect, head up, ears pricked. Then she prances, knee action high, like a show horse. The other deer follows. They break into a canter, leaping logs and streams. The rabbit and the goose watch, alert. Then, when the two deer break into a dead run, the goose takes to the air, honking and flapping, following them. The rabbit joins in, taking short cuts across the yard, dashing from side to side. For ten minutes the play goes on, to the obvious delight of all the participants.

Animals' joy in exercising their abilities exists in work as well as in play. Horses enjoy being ridden, sled dogs stand by their traces in anticipation of the run. The German word *funktionslust* expresses this pleasure that creatures derive from doing an act superlatively well. It is "functionlust" that impels skiers to climb a mountain in order to glide down its slopes. It is what makes tennis and golf pleasurable, as well as the playing of music, the writing of poems or the creation of forms of art. When a man does a kind of work well, it is functionlust that makes him derive pleasure from doing it. That is the reason why there is often more happiness derived from striving to attain a goal than from actually reaching it.

At the end of the last century a physician and psychologist, Madame Montessori, employed the principle of functionlust to teach deprived children in the slums in Rome. Before she formed her school, she had been engaged in studying and teaching mentally retarded children. At that time, there was a great deal of vandalism and delinquency among the children of the slum areas, much as there is in our country today. Dr. Montessori was asked to establish a school for the normal three- to seven-year-old children of the Roman tenements, whose working parents left them alone during the day. By keeping the children occupied, the owners of the tenement houses hoped to save the buildings from future vandalism and damage.

Dr. Montessori applied to the normal children the materials and methods that she had used with success in the education of the mentally retarded. As she expanded her unique system, she developed an understanding of children's spontaneous interest in learning. Her methods were very like those of her contemporary in America, John Dewey, who also emphasized freedom, self-activity, a measure of self-education, and the teaching of "practical life" activities. Madame Montessori's success far surpassed her own hopes and those of her sponsors. Not only were the Roman children distracted from vandalism, but they became avid pupils. Before the age of five, many of them had mastered the basics of counting, reading, and writing.

The Montessori achievement suggests that enrichment of the child's experience during preschool years may be an antidote for cultural deprivation. The deprivation, which often occurs in children in slum areas, results in serious and often irreversible retardation of their ability to learn, for if an infant, with normal potential to learn, is deprived of the early experiences which are the basis of later learning, he will grow up incapable of learning well.

In recent years, under the influence of the Swiss psychologist Jean Piaget, educators are belatedly beginning to appreciate the importance of the early years and to realize that children as young as three are capable of learning to read, write, typewrite, and play musical instruments. The changes brought about by exposure to an enriched environment early in life may result in an actual increase in the size of the brain, for the cortex of the brain of rats exposed from birth to rich environments has been found to be 4 percent larger than that of litter-mates reared alone in empty cages. As a result of these observations, it is likely that in the future the public school system will start at the nursery school age of two or three. What happens in these early years has so much effect on the child's subsequent ability to learn that a small investment in these years pays dividends throughout the entire period devoted to education. For this reason, if a choice had to be made between sending a child of mine to nursery school or to college, I would pick nursery school.

For many years it was accepted that the genes which carry the heredity of the individual fix his intellectual capacity. This is the concept of a genetically fixed Intelligence Quotient (IQ). While it is undoubtedly true that the genes determine the potential for learning, they do not guarantee that the individual will achieve that potential. A British study, made to determine the importance of early experience in later learning, indicated that the environment in which a child is reared has a profound effect on IQ and on subsequent ability to learn. The children were separated into an "upper class" and a "lower class" group, the occupations of their parents being taken as an index of social class. At six months and again at eighteen months of age, there was no significant difference in the average IQ's of the children of the two groups. But at three years and at five years, there were found to be significant social class differences. The upperclass children showed, on the average, a gain of 15 points in IQ, while in the lower class there was an average fall of 10 points. The changes were attributed to the stimulating environment and the rich vocabulary and use of language to which the one group was exposed, and the deprivations experienced by the other.

A study was made by psychologists of two groups of children in an orphanage. The first group of thirteen infants, aged from seven to thirty months, with IQ's averaging 64.3, were transferred from the orphanage to a school for the mentally retarded. A second group of twelve infants of approximately the same age, with IQ's averaging 13 points higher, were left in the orphanage. The first group of baby orphans received a great deal of attention from the older, brighter retarded girls, who became attached to them and played with them during the babies' waking hours. When both groups were retested, two to four years later, it was found that the children left in the orphanage had a lower IQ than at their first testing. All of the children transferred to the school for the mentally retarded showed higher IQ's, all but four of the thirteen gaining more than 20 points. A follow-up of the histories of the orphans later in life showed that in spite of the fact that the children who remained in the orphanage originally had higher IQ's than the others, half of them failed to complete the third grade and none reached high school. Five eventually became permanent wards of the state. In striking contrast, the median grade completed by the children sent to the school for the mentally retarded was the twelfth, four went on to college, and all became self-supporting.

In animals, the effect of early experience on the ability of an adult to solve problems is proportional to the amount of brain which is set aside for learning. The behavior of a turtle, which has little capacity for learning, cannot be changed significantly by experiences early in life. Rats, on the other hand, which are more intelligent, were found to be more skilled at solving problems when reared as pets than their littermates left in cages. In dogs, whose intelligence is higher than that of rats, the difference in ability to solve problems was even greater between those reared as pets and those that were confined. Since man's ability to learn excels that of all creatures, it is obvious that his early experiences are likely to have the greatest effect on ultimate performance.

Early deprivation not only affects the ability to learn well but also interferes with the development of what are generally considered to be innate action patterns. Eighty-five percent of the children in a Teheran orphanage were still unable to walk at the age of four. The bodies of these children were not restrained, but confined as they were, largely to their cribs, they had not had the experience of seeing people walking about. Having no mental image of walking, they did not try to do so. It has been suggested that control of muscular coordination may be less a matter of educating the child's muscles than of his having a clear image of what he is trying to do. The Hopi Indian babies, reared with their legs and arms restrained, but free to observe with eyes and ears what went on around them, were not a bit retarded when it came time to walk. They had been reared with things going on around them and they had developed interest in their environment.

Interest, curiosity, or some type of emotional motivation seems to be essential to the process of converting the transient, electrically recorded memory traces into long-lasting, chemically coded memories. In animals, there seems to be a sort of standard of interest that is built-in, like the regulators hunger and thirst, which control the levels of sugar or water in the blood and body fluids. When the input of interesting stimuli from the environment falls to a level below the innate standard of expectancy, the creature becomes restless and tries to correct the deficiency. If the input of interesting stimuli exceeds the expectancy, the creature also feels restless and withdraws from the source of stimuli until the innate standard is balanced again. If this applies to human beings, it is clear that children could be made restless by either too much or too little stimulation. Since the innate standard of interest of each child varies from that of the next, a wide choice must be offered in either seeking out or retreating from educational stimuli, so that each individual is satisfied in accordance with his particular need.

Montessori recognized that abilities do not develop in all individuals at the same time, and therefore she put children varying in age between three and seven in the same class. Within this group each child could find his own level of interest and ability. Thus he would participate in his own development rather than having it thrust upon him and would learn through his own curiosity rather than through a rigid schedule.

Since many types of behavior that are natural to children do not persist into adult life, a child cannot be judged by the standard set for adults. It is possible that if one extinguishes a certain supposedly undesirable pattern of behavior in a child, one may be destroying the foundation on which the development of another pattern is going to rest. The same situation exists physically in the development of a frog. If a pollywog's tail is cut off, the creature will grow into a frog without hind legs, for the cells destined to be the mature frog's legs are contained in the immature creature's tail.

There is an innate restlessness in children which the Montessori method recognized. The child was allowed to move about as long as he did not do so to the detriment of the work of others. Discipline was maintained through interest rather than punishment; learning was assumed to contain its own reward. Advantage was taken of the curiosity and spontaneous activity of a child, and this was allowed to motivate his learning. The function of the teacher was to provide materials and direct the activity into constructive channels. The child himself was to select what he would learn. This same principle was found to apply in a laboratory experiment with rats in regard to food. They were given an artificial diet which contained, in a number of separate feeders, each of the ingredients essential to maintain perfect physical condition. Each animal selected the proportion from the containers that was in almost exact accord with his ideal needs.

Principles of preschool education, similar to those developed by Montessori, have been employed by the federal program, Head Start, which is concerned with the economically and culturally deprived children of slum areas of this country. It has been reported that the average IQ of the Head Start children increased 8 to 10 points in the first year of the experiment in spite of the fact that most of the children were beyond the optimum age for obtaining good results.

Startling results have been attained by "programmed instruction" in which the act of learning is broken up into parts, each of which is reinforced individually and finally combined to produce the whole. B. F. Skinner of Harvard has trained pigeons to walk in a figure eight, the entire process of training requiring only five to ten minutes. Each time the pigeon makes a part of the desired response, such as turning in a clockwise direction, the act is reinforced by dispensing food. When that part is learned, the operator of the food dispenser begins to reinforce the counterclockwise turns. Finally the pigeon learns to do the two turns in succession and the figure eight as a whole is reinforced by further feeding. These principles have been applied successfully in training human idiots and emotionally disturbed children. Skinner thinks that this concept and certain new teaching machines ought to be used to teach normal children. However, he says, "We fear effective teaching, as we fear all effective means of changing human behavior." If Skinner is correct in his estimate of the efficiency of these methods of teaching, it is important to decide exactly what should be taught before they are employed.

In another study of the training process, pigeons were taught to discriminate without error between two disks of different colors. The birds were started with a red one that was brightly lit and a green one that was dark. The pigeon would peck the bright red disk and be rewarded. Soon it would peck the red disk instantly, but never the darkened green one. At this point the green disk was gradually illumined, until it was lit as brightly as the red. The pigeon, while responding to the red disk, disregarded the green entirely, never making an error. The bird never became "emotional" about mistakes, as did others who were punished when they pecked at the wrong disk and as a result learned more slowly.

Rewards on one hand and punishments on the other have for centuries been used to promote the process of learning in children. If punishments become associated with the material that the student fails to learn, he may be impelled to stay away from it and develop a "block." If the positive side of learning could be reinforced early, no time would need to be spent in extinguishing wrong patterns of behavior.

Punishment, unless it is a direct one, is not an effective way of extinguishing a bad pattern of behavior. The child who has been burned receives a direct type of punishment from the fire and learns to avoid it. Indirect punishment, however, such as spanking him later on for having played with matches, is seldom successful. Dog trainers know that if an animal will not come when you call him, it will do no good to punish him when he finally obeys. He may interpret the punishment as having been given because he came. A more effective way of training the dog is to arrange the process of learning so that it serves as its own reward.

Threats without punishment may be effective deterrents to undesirable behavior, but not for long. Experiments were done with birds, in which models of predators were shown repeatedly. The initial alarm response was found to wane rapidly through habituation. However, it was found that when a real predator, such as a snake, was shown to the birds, their alarm response was instant and did not wear off.

Curiosity is one of the strong incentives in life. If hungry rats are on their way to solving a problem which they know will result in food, and some new and interesting device is placed in their path, they will stop to investigate. If the contents of a child's reading, or the process by which he is learning to write, fascinate him, he will be impelled to continue.

The child's curiosity, as well as his ability to expand his vocabulary, are at their peak in the first years of school. If he has not learned to read well by the time he finishes third grade, the child rarely will develop into a good reader. In theory, it also seems that the larger the vocabulary of the books the better, as long as the basic concepts are within comprehension. Since new words are like a new language the earlier the child's vocabulary is learned the better will be his memory of the words, as well as his usage and pronunciation of them.

Pleasure in the act of learning is very like function-lust. If the process of learning in the child could be programmed so that from the first it would be rewarding and pleasurable, many of the problems of education might be solved. Long ago Montaigne, in his essay on the education of children, advised, "I would chuse to have the Pictures of Joy and Gladness in the Schools, together with *Flora* and the Graces; that where their Profit is, there might be their Pleasure."

CHAPTER FIVE

Higher Education

One had to cram all this stuff into one's mind, whether one liked it or not. This coercion had such a deterring effect that, after I had passed the final examination, I found the consideration of any scientific problems distasteful to me for an entire year.

—Albert Einstein

In thinking back over my experiences in grade school and high school, I cannot remember a single teacher who stimulated me intellectually, nor a text that fired my imagination. All I can recollect is the drudgery of classrooms and homework. At that period of my life I must have been in an intellectual blackout. Yet I was given creditable marks and had no trouble passing college entrance examinations.

The first flicker of excitement over learning came in my second year at college when I took a course entitled "The Science of Society," a combination of sociology, anthropology, and philosophy that was taught by a hardheaded German-born professor named Keller. He was a realist, skeptical of everything from religious beliefs to sex mores. His attitude, based on the then revolutionary writings of William Graham Sumner, opened for me a new world. From that time on I realized that it was possible to learn for the fun of learning. Needless to say my grades throughout the rest of college and medical school reflected this newfound interest.

I think my problem in the precollege years was that I was forced to remember so many facts and figures. Few principles were pointed out to me, or if they were I was unable to grasp their significance.

Almost all the names and dates that I learned in school have long since been forgotten, as have the details of what Keller taught me, but the skepticism of orthodox beliefs and the spirit of inquiry that I learned from him have stuck with me all my life. Education, it has been said, is what remains when a man has forgotten all he has been taught. This residue is the skill that has been acquired in dealing with facts. Attitudes and methods are in this connection more important than factual memory.

Slowness in learning is not necessarily a liability, for in the process of learning, it is not just remembering that counts. Forgetting must be reckoned with, too. This subject has been studied by B. J. Underwood, whose experiments indicate that forgetting proceeds at a constant rate that is quite independent of the speed with which the material was learned. A slow learner, provided he has learned something well, will remember the material just as long as a fast one. He might even remember longer, because he will be less apt to have "interference" from memories of things previously learned.

The "interference theory" implies that experiences, similar to the one a person is trying to recall, interfere with his ability to recall the one he wants. Thus, a nonsense syllable can be remembered for a long time if it is unique, but if it is one of many similar ones that have already been memorized, it is hard to bring it to mind. People are apt to remember ususual experiences for a lifetime and to forget those that were one of many similar to each other.

A bright child, who learns a great deal very fast, is likely to forget more rapidly than a slower one who learns less, because the bright child's memory contains much more material and hence many more interfering associations than the slower one's. These principles may explain why the majority of brilliant schoolchildren fare little or no better in later life than do those of average-learning ability and also help to account for the fact that as one gets older and has more and more experiences it becomes progressively more difficult to remember the recent ones.

Although a part of a person's ability to learn may be innate, the differences in different individuals tend to be equalized by other factors such as early training, emotional stability, and motivation. A recent study by

Dr. James W. Bartlett, associate dean of the University of Rochester School of Medicine, showed little consistent differences between the performance in medical school of a group of students who had unusually low scores on the Medical College Admission Test and those who had acceptable ones within wide limits. No correlation has been shown between academic performance as measured by grades and subsequent occupational success. It has also been found in an extensive government-sponsored study of schoolchildren that schools with widely varying characteristics, some generally considered to be "good" and some "bad," differed very little in their effects on their students, provided that the family backgrounds of the students were similar.

In most people it is either strong motivation or periodic repetition of material which fixes it in memory. Each repetition augments the capacity of the affected circuit to transmit the current. Cramming for an examination does not result in prolonged retention of the material studied. Even a well-learned language must be reinforced by occasional use or it will slip away. Slow learners can retain material as effectively as fast ones if they will go over it repeatedly.

The factors that determine whether or not an experience will be recorded as a permanent memory are poorly understood. It is not even known whether all memories are permanently recorded and lost to conscious recall only because of the inefficiency of the process of finding the one that is wanted, or whether the memory trace itself gradually disappears. There is some evidence to suggest that once a memory is fixed it is permanently stored. The Russian psychologist Aleksandr Luria has described the memory of one of his patients, "Mr. S.," a professional mnemonist who made his living by performing feats of memory on the stage. There appeared to be ". . . no limit either to the capacity of S.'s memory or to the durability of the traces he retained," Dr. Luria said. "Experiments indicated that he had no difficulty in reproducing any lengthy series of words whatever, even though these had originally been presented to him a week, a month, a year, or even many years earlier."

Penfield, in his operations on epileptic patients, also made observations which suggest that all experiences that reach the level of consciousness are stored in a person's brain for the rest of his life, even if they cannot be willfully recalled. When Penfield stimulated the cortex of the temporal lobe of the brain, his patients often had vivid recollections of events which had transpired many years before and had long since been dropped from conscious memory. One reported that fields and flowers and childhood friends came to her mind as in a moving picture, in such sequence and timing that it was as if the events were occurring again. It was as though Penfield's electrode cut in at random on a record, and that the patient saw and heard what had been experienced in some earlier time and felt the same emotions as then. These observations imply that even "forgotten" events of early life are permanently stored in the subconscious record of memory.

Since the brain's capacity to store the records of experiences is not infinite, as age advances the space available may become more and more limited. The British psychologist W. H. Thorpe says that most animals cannot learn as well when old as when young. In men in their twenties and thirties, some types of abilities are at their peak. The average age at which the Nobel Prize winners in physics published their important work is thirty-four years. It is possible that well-meaning educators are cluttering the minds of children and young adults with too many facts. Four centuries ago Montaigne noted this possibility, saying, "But let his Governor remember what is the true End of his Lessons, and that he do not so much imprint in his Pupil's Memory the Date of the Ruin of Carthage, as the Manners of Hannibal and Scipio, nor so much what place Marcellus died at, as why it was unworthy of his Duty that he die there." What Montaigne had in mind was the desirability of developing a student's ability to form general concepts, even though particulars are lost, a capacity that was conspicuously lacking in the fact-filled mind of Dr. Luria's mnemonist.

Although Penfield's observations suggest that memories are stored permanently, there is reason to believe that there are two types of memory, each with its own mechanism of storage. B. W. Agranoff, working with goldfish at the Michigan Institute of Mental Health, determined that there is a short-term variety of memory which is not permanently recorded, and after it has vanished, the space concerned with storing it may become available again for reuse. Dr. Agranoff thinks this short-term memory may be produced by changes in "electrical states, conformation changes in protein, or other readily reversible phenomena." He believes that to form the other, long-term kind of memory "requires changes of which protein synthesis is a part."

An example of the difference in the two types of memory is demonstrated when a person is struck unconscious by a blow on the head. When he regains consciousness, older, chemically stored memories are unaffected, but he is apt to remember nothing of what happened immediately before the accident. This phenomenon, known as retroactive amnesia, depends on the time it takes to convert the initial electrically stored memory into the more permanent chemically stored variety. When concussion occurs before the memory is transferred to the chemical variety, the memory trace is permanently lost.

Agranoff notes that "if what is considered motivation, affect, or 'emotional tone' fixes a temporary trace, it is then stored permanently." This is why a person is not able to recollect what he ate for supper a week earlier unless the memory was "set" by a special association of some kind. Agranoff likens the memory system to two tape recorders, in one of which the record is automatically erased after a certain period of time and is permanently lost unless the other recorder to which it is connected has duplicated the record and stored it permanently. It seems that some type of motivation, curiosity, or interest is necessary to convert the short-term to the long-term type.

One of the baffling features of memory is that as yet no one has been able to localize a precise area in the brain where it is stored. It seems to be widely dispersed throughout the brain. That is why, when large sections of the brain are destroyed, all memories are dimmed rather than specific ones lost.

In flatworms, memory appears to be stored throughout the entire body. If a worm is cut in two, memories of previous training remain in the worms that regenerate from both ends of the divided body. This has raised the question as to whether in human beings memory is stored in molecules of RNA, and is distributed widely in the brain instead of being contained in one small area. Since memory is chemical, however, and the space for storing it is not infinite, there may be a limit to the brain's capacity either to store or to retrieve it. But regardless of how memory is stored, what is most urgently needed is knowledge about the timings and sequences in which the child's brain is best fitted to record the various types of information that are necessary to the development of essential skills.

Every organism, in its growth from egg to adult, goes through the various stages through which its ancestors passed in the course of evolutionary development. This is Haeckel's biogenetic law, stating that "ontogeny recapitulates phylogeny." Since learning depends upon the biochemical functions of the brain, the development of the ability to learn specific subjects may also follow this fundamental law. The sequence in which the human race acquired its symbolism and knowledge of the world may be the one best adapted to the average individual's learning ability. In the case of language, this is obviously true, for language was the first type of symbolism developed and it is best learned in a child's earliest years.

If science could be taught in terms of history, showing how the train of human thought led to the concepts which exist today, it might be easier for the child to understand. If history were used as a means of constructing an image of the world, all of the disciplines could be constantly reinforced. In each period studied, mathematics, science, political history, and literature could be brought up again, as their development was discussed. This process, as viewed by educator J. S. Bruner, of Harvard, is like a spiral, with the child "coming back again and again to the same subject on a higher level of maturity." Such a system might provide an answer to parents' and teachers' complaints about children's lack of interest in learning.

At the turn of the century, John Dewey said, "We even go so far as to assume that the mind is naturally averse to learning, which is like assuming that the digestive organs are averse to food and have to be coaxed or bullied into having anything to do with it. . . . We fail to see that such aversion is in reality a condemnation of our methods, a sign that we are presenting material for which the mind in its existing state of growth has no need, or else presenting it in such ways as to cover up the real need. . . . Surely the adult is much more likely to learn the things befitting him when his hunger for learning has been kept alive continuously than after a premature diet of adult nutriment had deadened his desire to know." The biological counterpart of Dewey's principle is seen when injection of an adult frog's tissues arrests the development of a frog embryo.

Schools with rigid curricula that force all children, regardless of their aptitudes, into the same mold, expose many of the slower learners to material that they are not yet mature enough to find interesting. If a child is slow in comprehending mathematics, as many are, his failure to pass the subject excludes him from the study of sciences for which mathematics has been made a prerequisite. As a result he grows up ignorant not only of the nature of the world he lives in, but also of his nature. This ignorance is unnecessary, since a basic comprehension of most sciences can be obtained without more than an elementary understanding of mathematics. Bruner says, "Any subject can be taught effectively in some intellectually honest form to any child at any stage of development."

Even a low IQ does not necessarily preclude high intellectual attainment in specific fields. Recently psychologists reported a pair of identical twins who were termed "genius idiots." While their intelligence quotients were 60, the level of idiocy, they had a mental capacity for understanding numbers that was unsurpassed by the most skilled mathematicians. The twins had a "calendar sense," which enabled them, without pencil or paper, instantly to say what day of the week any date in history fell upon. They even made allowances for the changes made in the calendar and could calculate back into ancient times. It seems inconsistent to deny higher education to such children, with unequal distribution of talents, and yet to provide special facilities for those with other types of handicaps, such as blindness, deafness, or dyslexia. Regardless of how many "blind spots" a student may have, a talent, if fully developed, can make him a valuable member of society.

Little is known about what happens to a child's capacity to learn about a subject when he is not presented with the opportunity to study it at the appropriate time in his intellectual development. In this connection, it is not reassuring to think of what happens to persons born blind as a result of cataracts. After being totally blind from birth to between the ages of three and forty-three, a group of them were operated upon. Although they developed vision, they still could not see. They had to learn and it took months and years; many never learned. Some wished to be blind again, saying that sight was like a "confusing and unbearable noise." The image of the world that they had built up was organized by all of their senses other than sight. When they could see, their image became confused. It may be equally confusing to a person brought up with no knowledge of mathematics or science to find himself in a world which cannot be fully appreciated without these concepts. Bewildered, they are driven to existentialism or to acceptance of some spiritualistic mystique.

Modern man is living in a period of such rapid change that startling developments are overthrowing most of the conventional laws of mathematics and the physical sciences. New interpretations of history are constantly being made. Truth is becoming progressively more difficult to define. Sir George Pickering, past president of the British Medical Association, stated that there was no such thing as absolute truth, and that "the true aim of the teacher must be to impart an appreciation of method and not a knowledge of facts." The philosopher William James said that " 'the true' is only the expedient in the way of our thinking. . . . The 'facts' themselves meanwhile are not true. They simply are."

It seems that from the beginning, students should be accustomed to regarding what is taught as probabilities rather than truths. To serve this purpose, there might be employed in every school an "anti-teacher" whose function would be to try to explode all dogma taught by the other teachers and to demonstrate that everything can be viewed from more than one angle. Anti-teaching might prevent the circuits involved in learning from becoming too fixed in set beliefs.

My father, who was a surgeon and biologist, used to

tell me that the life of what was accepted as a physiologic fact was five years. Today its average life is even shorter. When concepts are changing this fast, it is a disadvantage to have fixed beliefs that are difficult to change. What is needed is a system of understanding in which a disproved belief can be dropped and replaced by one more in harmony with newly evolving concepts.

Ingenuity and inventiveness depend on the ability to acquire new types of learning and to make associations of a kind that cannot be taught in schools. Charles Huggins, Nobel Laureate, surgeon, and scientist at the University of Chicago, said that although creativeness could not be taught, the techniques of discovery were "contagious to the young." The question is whether creativeness cannot be extinguished by spending too many years in formal postgraduate education devoted more to obtaining grades or degrees than to original work of one's own.

The term orthogenesis refers to the progressive evolution of a species in a certain direction. It was responsible for the extreme and ultimately encumbering size of the antlers of the Irish elk, a creature that probably was rendered extinct by this feature. Orthogenesis may occur too in the evolution of customs, such as religious rites, when in successive generations they develop progressively and sometimes perniciously in a certain direction, regardless of the influence of environmental factors or natural selection. Modern man may now be in a period in which, with no regard for basic values, he is committed to an ever-greater prolongation of the period of life devoted to higher education of the conventional type. Fifty years ago, a high school diploma was considered a prerequisite for most types of employment. Twenty years ago, a college degree was required. Now it is a master's. Tomorrow's employer may ask for a doctorate. Today's children are spending most of their potentially creative years in preparing themselves for their careers. No less an authority than James B. Conant has recently challenged the widely accepted premise about the value of college education, asking, "Does not our present pattern, which involves a high-prestige value for the bachelor's degree, postpone too long entry into a significant career for many youths?"

Birds, if hand-fed for too long a period, may lose their ability to feed themselves in the wild. When chicks are fed artificially and not allowed to peck at grains for two weeks after hatching, it is impossible to teach them to eat except by an indirect and time-consuming process of training. Old cage birds who have gotten their food from the same tray for many years may refuse to eat from the ground or even from a different tray.

Prolonged restraint of swallows far beyond the natural time for flying interferes with their ability to develop skill in flying. In animals, there are critical periods during which skills of various types are best perfected. If the same principles apply to human beings, one of the greatest challenges to educators is to define these periods for each of the numerous human skills.

It has been said that nowadays man looks to education for salvation, as he once looked to religion or to a political ideology. This is not a reassuring analogy, in the light of some of the religious and political practices which developed during the Middle Ages, and of the abnegations and distortions of life which ensued. Perhaps, in a few decades, students will enter universities as the monks once entered monasteries, not to prepare themselves for life, but as a way of life. Nor should it be forgotten that some historians believe that the Mandarin system, in which applicants for positions in the political hierarchy of China spent more than half of their lives studying for competitive examinations, was one of the reasons why China remained a sleeping giant for so many centuries. Overeducation might be as fatal to the development of a society as it is known to be to certain individuals who go from degree to degree, and then straight into teaching, without ever leaving the shelter of the university or testing their learning against the realities of life.

If we continue to emphasize higher education and persist in neglecting the importance of what is learned in the first few years of life, it is unlikely that we will ever accomplish our educational aims. It is important too that we develop a better understanding of the process of learning. Ultimately this may be accomplished by studying the chemical changes involved in establishing nerve circuits.

Years ago, Paul Weiss, a pioneer in the physiology of the nervous system, noticed that when the skin of a frog's back was touched, the frog scratched the stimulated area with his hind limb. When the belly was stimulated, he scratched with the forelimb. Weiss took off part of the skin of a frog's flank and replaced it, reversing its position, so that the belly part was where the back part used to be. When the frog's nerves grew back into the skin, stimulation of the patch of back skin that was now on the belly produced the type of reflex that normally came from stimulating the skin of the back. The nerves had made connections with the skin in such a way that the "back nerves" had found "back skin" and "belly nerves" had found "belly skin." When Weiss transplanted forelimbs of salamanders, reversing their directions, each muscle-controlling cell in the brain became connected with the muscle to which it had originally belonged, even when the position of the muscles was reversed. When the salamander tried to move ahead, the limb pushed it backward.

It has been suggested that there are chemical qualities in the skin, and also in the nerves that supply it, which determine the way the skin will be connected to the centers of the brain. This is possible, it is thought, because each spot on the skin has a unique chemical makeup or "flavor." The same "flavor" is thought to be present in the nerve that goes to it and in the corresponding center to which the nerve is connected. Thus it appears that in the development of the embryo, the cortex of the brain and the lower centers of the nervous system undergo chemical changes that parallel, in miniature, those that occur on the body surfaces. As a result, the nervous system forms a map-like projection of the body, each part connected, by means of special chemical affinities, with the part of the body which has the corresponding "flavor."

The concept of the brain as a map of the body implies that nerves carry not only electrical impulses but also chemicals between the brain cells and the body. It is perhaps for this reason that if a salamander's leg is amputated, it will grow a new one, but if the cells which give rise to the nerves that go to the stump are destroyed, the leg will not regenerate. The map of the leg that contains the chemical instructions for growing the new leg is stored in the nervous system. If there are no nerves connecting the stump with the cells in which the instructions are stored, regeneration is impossible. Similar principles may apply to storage of information about the environment, the brain mapping it out in memory just as it does the body. It is the chemistry and the timing of this essential process that we do not yet understand.

Although billions of dollars are being spent on medical research, and billions more in the race to put a man on the moon, little is being allotted for research into either the mechanism of learning or the effectiveness of teaching. Money is poured into the construction of buildings for high schools and colleges as well as into the training of teachers, but no one has yet determined by scientific methods how the various subjects should be taught or at what stage of mental development the student is best fitted to learn each. Before using the powerful means that are now available to alter the patterns of man's behavior, controlled experiments in education must be done. They must be undertaken with full knowledge that their effects on the behavior of the individuals involved may be irreversible. The discoveries made in this field could produce changes in the organization of society as striking as those which accompanied the Industrial Revolution. Wilder Penfield said, "Adjust the time and the manner of learning; then you may double your demands and your expectations."

CHAPTER SIX

Emotional Stability

*If each of us can be helped by science to
live a hundred years, what will it profit
us if our hates and fears, our loneliness
and remorse will not permit us to enjoy
them?*
—David Neiswanger, President,
The Menninger Foundation

Last spring Helga and I bought a baby black swan that
gave us an insight into the irreversible changes that
can be wrought by deprivation. Before the bird came
to us, he had been hatched in an incubator and reared
for three weeks in a brooder with no companions. We
kept him in a pen in the kitchen where he could get
used to people being about and whenever we went
outdoors, we took him along. But wherever the swan
was put, he finally would be found in a corner, with
his head to a wall, chirping to himself as he had in the
incubator box. From time to time he would go to the
pond to swim, but if there were other birds there, he

struck at them with his bill to drive them off. The bird became such a menace that we reluctantly returned him to his original owner.

The black swan's unnatural, withdrawn behavior, and his failure to develop normal affection or even tolerance for other creatures, resulted from his early solitary confinement. The same thing will happen to a dog if it is reared alone in the austere environment of a kennel. It never becomes at ease with people and will always be shy, cower, and have a tendency to snap nervously. No amount of love or kindness can overcome these traits; the animal is doomed for life to be an emotional cripple. If a dog is to be a household pet, it should not be deprived, while still a puppy, of associations with the family. After five months, its ways will be set, and if not in contact with people, its personality will show a steady deterioration. Similar changes in behavior were observed in Harlow's monkeys when they were separated from their mothers and infant peers.

Human babies reared for six months or more in orphanages without individualized loving may have their emotional development seriously blighted. The British psychologist Bowlby says that separation of orphan children from the "mother figure" for six months or more during the first five years of life is an important cause of later delinquency. Children so treated develop into creatures devoid of affection, unable to feel either love or guilt.

It may be that the Age of Anxiety in which we are

said to be living is due less to the complexities of our
society than to the way our children are reared. Perhaps the brief attention an infant gets when fed by a
pillow-propped bottle gives him less security than the
prolonged mothering associated with nursing at the
breast. Children born in less hurried centuries may
have grown up with fewer anxieties because their
cradles stood in the kitchens, where there was continual activity.

From the standpoint of survival, the greatest disaster
that could befall a baby would be to be abandoned.
Noise and activity may reassure the child that he has
not been forgotten. The old-fashioned three-genera-
tion home had a built-in baby sitter in the person of
the unhurried grandmother. In some respects, a
society with a "low" standard of living and in which
the mothers do not leave the home to work may be better adapted to rearing stable children than one with
a supposed "high" standard.

In the obstetrical departments of many hospitals it is
the policy to separate mother and baby at birth and
bring the baby to the mother only for short visits. It is
beginning to be thought that this practice is damaging
to the delicate relationship between mother and child.
If a baby goat or sheep is separated from its mother for
a few hours after birth, the mother usually rejects it
permanently. If the same is true to any degree in human beings, it is possible that the failure of maternal
instinct that so often results in neglect of the child is
attributable not to a fault of the instinct but to the

practice of not keeping mother and baby together. From the standpoint of reinforcing the mother's instinctive feelings, if the baby is not allowed to be with her and be nursed by her it is as though the baby had died.

Neglect of children can cause more than mere changes in their personalities; life itself may be at stake. Dr. Spitz reported that in a foundling home in which the babies were given excellent nursing care and nutrition, but no mother's care, the mortality rate of the children was 37 per cent in two years. Five of the twenty-one children were unable to walk at the age of two to four years, only nine could eat with a spoon, six could not talk at all, and most had vocabularies of three to five words. The deterioration of these children was progressive and was not reversed when they were given a better environment after the age of one and a half years.

I have observed orphanage-reared children at the ages of ten to twelve, who were referred to the hospital for treatment. Their behavior was like that of our young black swan, hostile, withdrawn, and aloof. Emotions seem to be like languages in that they must be learned in the first few years of life or they can never be expressed fully and with the proper accent. Failure to have a normal environment to learn in is a major cause not only of emotional instability but also of phobias, overaggressiveness, anxiety, and obsessions. These neuroses, like their counterparts in animals, usually are the result of deprivations or of abnormal experiences encountered early in life.

Half a century ago, Pavlov described conditioned reflexes in animals, showing that if a bell were rung every time food was presented to a dog, the dog soon came to associate the sound of the bell with eating. Once this association was established, the dog salivated whenever the bell was rung, even though no food was given. Today psychologists, working along the same lines as Pavlov, are beginning to view behavior as being made up of conditioned responses and habits learned by the individual to enable him to adapt to his environment. The habits that are maladapted produce what is termed abnormal behavior. Neuroses, therefore, are nothing more than misdirections of the normal process of learning.

When a young child is reared without the security that comes from being loved, he is apt to develop anxiety. Just as a strong emotion "sets" the memory of a trivial event that otherwise would be forgotten, so also the emotion of anxiety "sets" in the child's mind the pattern of behavior that he used to cope with his problem. Through repetition, this manner of coping may become a habit.

Habits are the foundation on which behavior is built. If a child's environment is abnormal at the time he is establishing his habits, the habits may reflect this abnormality. When the habits persist even after the environment has returned to normal the resulting behavior is maladapted and hence is judged abnormal or neurotic.

Since habits can often be changed, many neurotic people in the course of time improve with or without deconditioning or any other kind of treatment. This is not always the case, however; some never make a satisfactory adjustment to society. It has been estimated that nearly three out of four of the people who fail in their jobs do so not because of a lack of ability to perform but because emotional instability interferes with their interpersonal relationships. Thus if children are reared to be emotionally unstable, it is not only their enjoyment of life but even their ability to support themselves that is at stake.

Although it is difficult to compensate fully for deprivations encountered in childhood, this does not mean that all the ensuing neuroses are incurable. Moreover, many abnormalities of behavior arise as a result of situations encountered in adult life and either correct themselves when the circumstances change, or are correctable by appropriate reassurance or deconditioning treatment. The latter, in the opinion of many psychotherapists of the behavioral school, is more effective than psychoanalysis. As H. J. Eysenck, professor of psychology at London University, has put it, "It is an established fact that many neurotics get better without any form of treatment whatever, and that patients treated by psychoanalysis have not been shown to fare any better than those treated by other methods or not at all. If those who were psychoanalyzed do improve, a high proportion relapse within a few years. It has been shown too that psychoanalysis may, in certain cases, even have a negative effect and make the patient less likely to recover."

Dr. A. Krev, research psychiatrist at Columbia University, who has made extensive studies of psychiatric treatment abroad, notes that in countries other than the United States, psychoanalysis is often regarded not as an effective treatment but as a "sort of cult." In this country too, there is a trend in the medical profession to rely less on psychoanalysis and more on the modern methods of therapy including what have been called "short cuts" to the Freudian approach and, more recently, the newly developed behavior therapy.

Behavior therapy was introduced in 1958 by Joseph Wolpe, then of the department of psychiatry of the University of Witwatersrand, South Africa, and now at Temple University. Wolpe made cats neurotic by confining them in small cages and subjecting them to electric shocks. The animals reacted violently, rushed to and fro, clawed at the roof, floor and sides of the cage, crouched, trembled, howled, and spat. After a number of shocks the cats exhibited the same behavior whenever they were put in the cages, even if they were not shocked. Once the pattern of behavior had become established, prolonged confinement without shocking did not diminish the neurotic behavior of the cats, nor did the passage of time result in any improvement. Even if conditioned animals had been starved for seventy-two hours they would not eat meat dropped in front of them in the cage. Long absence from the cage did not weaken the response.

Dr. Wolpe next attempted to extinguish the cats' neuroses by substituting for the anxiety reaction a new set of behavior patterns that would be antagonistic to the behavior induced by anxiety. He starved the cats until they were hungry and then began to feed them in an area near to the cage. Gradually he moved the food closer to the cage and finally into it. Soon the cats were eating in the cage and no longer showed any signs of the anxiety that had been induced by the shocks. By that time the cage had become associated in the cats' mind with eating, a response that was so antagonistic to anxiety that it could not coexist with it and therefore replaced it.

Nearly fifty years ago, J. B. Watson reported that a child named Little Albert, who had been conditioned to exhibit great fear of a white rat, was deconditioned from his rat phobia by giving him chocolate candy whenever the rat appeared. This was the first human application of the "reciprocal inhibition" treatment of a phobia.

Recently a case of deconditioning by "aversion therapy" was employed by Drs. Glynn and Harper. The male patient was a transvestite who could not resist wearing his wife's clothes. He was asked to dress in them, was surrounded with female effects, and then was given repeated doses of apomorphine, a drug that induces nausea and vomiting. After four days, he exhibited revulsion at the sight of female clothes and did not, during a long period of subsequent observation, show any desire to wear them again. This aversion principle is the one commonly used by farmers to break their dogs of killing chickens: they tie a dead chicken around the dog's neck and leave it there until it decomposes.

Behavior therapy is based on the assumption that neuroses are unadaptive reactions learned in anxiety-generating situations. Since these neuroses have been acquired at a primitive subconscious level, they can be reversed only through applying a similar learning process at the same level. This explains why neuroses cannot be overcome by appealing to reason. If the stimulus that triggers the abnormal behavior is to be abolished, it has to become associated with a new type of response that is antagonistic to the old one. When this occurs the former neurotic reaction is not merely suppressed, but abolished.

Although it is too early yet to say how successful behavior therapy in humans will be, it is an example of the trend in psychiatry away from Freudian psychoanalysis. Psychotherapists of the behavioral school do not deny that psychoanalysis is sometimes helpful, but they attribute its beneficial effects to accidental deconditioning which takes place during the process. All of them agree with Freud's insistence that the experiences of the first five years of life are the foundations upon which the structure of the personality stands. These, in turn, rest on the bedrock of an immutable genetic code. No sharp line divides the "racial learning," transmitted in the genes, and the learning acquired in the first years of experience. Neither of these types of learning can ever be recalled consciously as memories. They are fixed in the brain at subconscious levels and the patterns established there cannot be changed by an act of will, any more than a neuromuscular reflex can voluntarily be suppressed.

Although most abnormal behavior is the result of neuroses, psychoses can cause it too. These are true mental diseases, like schizophrenia or severe depression. Unlike the neuroses, they seem to have no counterpart in animals. Some of them seem to have a genetic basis, for often they show a tendency to run in families. Seven of forty-seven persons born of schizophrenic mothers and separated from them at birth became schizophrenic as compared with none of fifty persons separated in a similar way from non-schizophrenic mothers.

Another major psychosis is the type of depression that bears no close relationship to events in the environment. It has, like schizophrenia, a familial tendency and perhaps a chemical cause. The periodic variations in mood that occur in people with depressions may be the result of some still undefined cycle in the body's chemistry similar to that which produces the depression or tension that some women experience before menstrual periods.

Since depressions are not mere reactions to environment, psychotherapy is of little value. They are corrected more effectively by one of the antidepressive drugs, like chlorpromazine. When drugs of this class are given to guinea pigs being reared in solitary confinement, they prevent the "psychotic" changes that otherwise develop. If the depression is a "reactive" type and is due to a series of disastrous experiences rather than the result of inner causes, psychotherapy, reassurance, and the healing that comes with the passage of time are indicated, rather than drugs or electric shock therapy.

Certain features of depression and altered moods are not understood. In the spring and fall, there is a restlessness which most humans share with the migratory birds. On gray rainy days, people become depressed. When the first warm sunshine of spring comes, humans and animals alike are exuberant. Perhaps these feelings well up from primitive centers where instincts lie buried. They may be evoked by association, or perhaps, as is the case with birds, by responses of endocrine glands to the longer hours of sunlight. In any event, chemicals are involved in the making of moods. From earliest time man has used them to cheer himself, in the form of beer, spirits, and wine.

Although suicides in adults are almost always caused by mental disease, rather than by simple situational depressions of mood, the genes for self-destruction may be present in the species. Some people seem to court danger for the sheer pleasure of it, when they go cliff-climbing or cave-exploring, auto and motorcycle racing or sky-diving. Many of history's heroes have displayed death-defying patterns of behavior, a member of a platoon throwing himself on a hand grenade to protect the others, or Horatius at the bridge over the Tiber, standing against the enemy.

Animals, at times, sacrifice themselves in defense of territory or their young. Tales are told of cats returning to burning barns for their kittens and of stallions attacking predators who threaten their herds of mares. The survival value of altruism and self-sacrifice may be explained by the assumption that the individual who loses his life defending his family group will preserve their genes, including those which caused his altruism. But it is likely that the increasing frequency of suicide in children is not so much genetic as the result of pressures at home and excessive competition for academic honors. It now stands third as a cause of death in the fifteen-to-nineteen-year age group.

There are certain aberrations of behavior that are neither genetic nor due to environment, but are the result of injuries incurred some time before the baby was born or at the moment of birth. One of these, due to damage to the brain, results in what is termed the "overactive child." For many years educators and psychologists have recognized that there are certain children who cannot remain quiet. No matter how great the reward or how severe the punishment, they do not seem able to control the urge to move about. This behavior, which in a mild form is not uncommon, is caused by the same type of injury that in extreme form causes a child to be spastic or to be afflicted with uncontrollable contortions. The part of the brain that controls motion has been damaged, with the result that muscular activity is released. The child is impelled to get up and move about.

Because most overactive children tend to be normal in other respects, their parents and teachers often do not understand that there is a physical cause for the restlessness. The situation in the home may become intolerable, as the adults quarrel about how the child should be handled. For years the high incidence of broken marriages, caused by the parents' disagreement over how to solve these insoluble problems, led psychiatrists to believe that the child's behavior was the result of emotional tension in the home. Now that the electroencephalogram is available to show the physical abnormality of the child's brain, his restlessness can be explained on the basis of the injury. The parents, assured, need only wait for the passage of time to curb the overactivity, which eventually abates.

Several types of mental retardation are related to hereditary deficiencies in the action of enzymes. Others are due to chromosomal abnormalities or viral infections incurred at a critical stage of fetal development. All can be recognized and the diagnosis confirmed by laboratory tests. The parents of these individuals, once shadowed by guilt, now understand that their responsibility is not for the composition of their baby, but only for its care after it is born.

By the time a child reaches six years of age, and is beyond the stage of childhood amnesia, the basis of his emotional behavior has been established. From this age until puberty, he is apt to go along on an even plane, stable or unstable, as the case may be. Then, at puberty, there comes a feeling of independence, especially in boys. Biologically, the adolescent is ready to leave home and become the father of children. If, at this time, his efforts to obtain independence are suppressed, the development of self-reliance and individuality may suffer, as was shown with Harlow's baby monkeys that were mothered too long without contact with their peers.

In this country the legal obligations of parenthood are such that a child is not permitted to strike out early for himself. In most trades he cannot get full-time employment until he is old enough to be insured, usually at eighteen. Parents' impatience with their teen-age children's behavior may be in part innate, for there is no animal except man who continues to care for offspring after they reach sexual maturity. In some cases it might be better for parents and children alike if the parents rebelled against their children and threw them out of the home as soon as they reach maturity instead of waiting for the children to rebel and leave. For this to become effective, the legal aspects of parental responsibility for teen-age children would have to be redefined and it might be necessary for the Government to organize a program that combined work and education so that the children would live in a youth community where they could learn skills, or practice trades, or go on with higher education.

Edmund Leach, anthropologist at Cambridge University, notes that the family has for centuries been the basis of Western society, but points out that this is not true in all cultures and that in this age the "narrow privacy" of the family group may be the source of much of our discontent. Children, he thinks, should grow up in a larger, more relaxed group, centered in the community, like the Israeli kibbutz, and he notes also that almost everywhere, outside the centers of Western capitalism, "the normal emphasis of education is on group rather than individual identity." A system of this type, in which children in the city slums were cared for and educated first in nurseries, then in day schools, but were with their families every evening, might compensate for the breakdown of family life. It could instill in the next generation skills in learning and a spirit of cooperation that seems impossible to attain when children of broken families grow up deprived of love and of training in the use of the tools that are essential to success in modern life. Without these there is no motivation to work, and as Rufus Mayfield, a twenty-one-year-old Washington Negro, recently told Stewart Alsop in an interview for *The Saturday Evening Post*, "After thirty, maybe twenty-five, a man living on his wits reaches a point where he just won't hold a regular job. You've got to catch them young."

Regardless of whether the trouble is with the family, the community, or the school, the fact remains that if we decided how we wanted our children to behave we could probably arrange their upbringing so that they would behave in the chosen manner. This would, of course, require a consensus and the full cooperation of parents, relatives, educators, and the community at large. The trouble is that each of these important elements tends to work against the next, the family urging the child to cooperate, the school fostering competitiveness, the community introducing a variety of distracting aims that may be at variance with those propounded by family and school. It is quite natural that in the midst of this confusion children grow up with no clear image either of what is expected of them or of what they want to do. Leach thinks that it is the educators who are most a fault, for in school, "The aim is to discover and cultivate the powers of latent leadership in the few with total disregard for the emotional suffering that this imposes on the many." Again, what in children appears to be emotional instability may well be the result of adults' well-intended but damaging efforts. One of society's major challenges is to direct these efforts along lines that are more scientific and effective.

Many psychologists believe that the scientific exploration of behavior cannot begin until the notion of "free will" is excluded. In the philosophical sense in which the term is used, it means that a person makes a decision spontaneously and "free from restraints, compulsions or any antecedent conditions." Opposed to this concept is the doctrine of determinism which assumes that the decision was made in accordance with previous conditioning.

The work of H. S. Liddell of Cornell shows that conditioning of animals in certain neurotic patterns of behavior may cause them to follow these patterns repetitively in spite of invariable, painful indirect forms of punishment. If habitual crime is a form of neurosis, it is understandable why 70 per cent of the felons in federal institutions have been in prison before and nearly 50 per cent of those now imprisoned will be back. It is also clear why, in England, the abolition of capital punishment has not resulted in an increase in the incidence of murders. The criminal's lack of a sense of guilt is rather like the experience of a patient with an injury of the brain, reported by Sir Russell Brain. The man, although conscious, was aware of only half of his body. After taking a bath, he would dry the half he was aware of, disregarding the other half. Perhaps, as a child, the criminal had experienced such deprivation that he grew up as unaware of either good or evil as Sir Russell's patient was of the other half of his body. In these circumstances the criminal can hardly be held accountable for his lack of conscience or for his antisocial behavior.

Many of the acts that we classify as criminal are in part, at least, instinctive. Once when I was a small child and was visiting an aunt, on my departure I packed into my suitcase all of the small articles in her house that I particularly admired. I had no notion that this was stealing. My behavior was like that of a squirrel who continues to collect nuts and put them away in his hoard as long as they are offered, no matter how plentiful his supply. When I was in boarding school, one of my classmates systematically robbed his friends of neckties and socks, storing the loot in his bureau drawer. Once a week, all of us would go there, sort out the clothes, and retrieve our own. The activity seemed to have nothing to do with need. This klepto- mania may be the result of a normal hoarding instinct grown too strong. Regardless of its cause, in the adult human being it is almost impossible to correct.

Crime does not seem to be the monopoly of the persistent or professional criminal, and in most cases it seems to be the result of early experience rather than of a genetic fault. It may be that present-day children are becoming imprinted with a tendency to accept crime and violence as a means to an end. More than ever in history it has become a part of children's play. It is upon the television screen in the news coverage of war and in the screen dramas that they watch continu- ally. Many of their toys are replicas of weapons, and they are learning how to use them.

Experiments have been conducted with two groups of chimpanzees, one having been reared with sticks to play with and the other with none. When the two groups were tested to see which could use sticks to the best advantage in securing an object set out of reach, the animals that had grown up with the sticks succeeded immediately. Their minds had been pre- pared, just as our children's minds are being prepared to use lethal weapons.

It is reported by J. Edgar Hoover that the incidence

of serious crime has spiraled upward since 1958 at a rate of five times that of the population's increase. Part of this may be the result of the social disorganization produced by one of the greatest migrations of history, that of the tens of millions from the South to the North, and from the farms to the slums of the industralized cities. In these crowded areas, "gangs" are apt to form among the teen-age population. According to Dr. S. Downes, of the London School of Economics, most gangs are adolescent peer groups and a part of the normal social activity of youth. They can be distinguished from true gangs of delinquents, because the latter are rare, have leaders, a definite membership, and persist for a long time. The peer-group gangs are loosely organized and come and go. Children enter them at the stage when they become teen-agers and are between the period of dependency on their parents and the time when they will assume the responsibilities of adulthood. With their peers of the same age, sex, and social status, the adolescents experience for the first time relationships embodying equality and democracy. Often within this structure are two or three seriously disturbed boys who have a bad influence on the short-term members. The results are apt to be the publicized garg wars and riots.

We have often observed that when a wild wood duck is introduced into the society of the hand-reared ones on our pond, the tame ones become nervous. Eventually the strange duck tames down, but the result is a flock somewhat wilder than it had been. Similar observations have been made with humans. When Redl introduced a disturbed boy into a group of normal children, he found that instead of the abnormal child changing his behavior to conform to the others, he persisted in it and induced disturbed behavior in the rest of the group.

It is difficult and sometimes impossible to change the nature of a seriously disturbed child. Perhaps the best way to eradicate delinquency in a group is to concentrate on locating the truly abnormal ones and remove them. The principle is that of finding the rotten apple in the barrel and eliminating it to save the rest from spoiling. This method is being applied in Newark, New Jersey, in a new type of rehabilitation institution called Essexfield. The premise is that many juvenile delinquents are not antisocial, and their seeming lawlessness is only a type of conformity to the values of their peer society. At Essexfield, delinquent boys are placed in a nucleus of ones already on the way to being successfully reformed. As the boys are discharged, new delinquents are added to the group. If they do not conform to the improved behavior pattern of the group, they are transferred to correctional institutions. The salvage rate has been 88 per cent as compared with the usual 25 to 50 per cent.

It cannot be assumed that disturbed behavior in modern society is the inevitable result of tensions and worries in the atomic age. Tensions and concern for survival must have been far greater in the feudal days, when wars between neighboring clans were almost continual, than they are today. Anxieties must have been keen among the serfs, whose lives often lay in the hands of irresponsible masters. Epidemics of small-pox and the Black Death periodically decimated populations. In modern times, however, there are factors in the urban environment which contribute to nervous tensions. The noise of the streets and the restlessness, so foreign to nature, are not conducive to tranquility.

Environment can produce a striking effect upon social behavior. V. H. Denenberg showed that when emotionally disturbed baby rats were liberated in a rich environment and supplied with what rats enjoy, recovery of emotional stability was much more rapid than when they were left in a barren test cage. In the first book of Samuel it is said, "It came to pass, when the evil spirit from God was upon Saul, that David took an harp, and played with his hand: so Saul was refreshed and was well, and the evil spirit departed from him."

Much of the art and music and architecture of our present environment seem not to be symbols of order and reality, but of discord and discontent. Our monumental buildings do not reflect the harmonious lines and intricate patterns of nature, but are harsh, repetitive, and irritating. In Ville Saint Marie, in newly built downtown Montreal, the facades of the great buildings, with their endlessly repeated, regular rows of windows, are alien to anything occurring in nature. On a recent visit, as I looked up at them, I felt dizzy, irritable, and bewildered. I was reminded of the effect that repetitive flashes of light have on the brain, sometimes causing convulsions, as happened during World War II in France to soldiers who were riding motorcycles at fast speeds while the sun was slanting through the regularly-spaced Normandy poplars that lined the roads. Occasionally they were seized with convulsions induced by the regular flashes of sunlight, and accidents occurred.

If children are reared in surroundings with qualities of disharmony, it is likely that this will be reflected in their lives and in what they create. Much of the contemporary art and music seems bent upon making the beholder feel estranged and confused rather than contented and elevated. City planner Constantinos Doxiadis says that nobody has yet been able to convince him that many of modern man's phobias are not due to the noise, filth, and ugliness that surround him.

The appreciation of natural beauty is similar in all races of man. Human beings everywhere are struck by the splendor of a sunset, the promise of a dawn, the majesty of a tree. These are universal realities. However, the symbols that one man makes to express his feelings are not always recognized or appreciated by another. To the Oriental ear, the music that stirs a Westerner deeply may be meaningless. The same may be true of art which does not represent nature in a recognizable form. Since it has been built symbol upon symbol, only the few who have been tutored understand it.

In every human being there is an innate desire for

perfection, a functionlust that is gratified in performing feats of coordination. It is inherent not only in the movements themselves but in the things done or made by them, resulting in the true arts. Perhaps this is the basis of man's appreciation of poetry, painting, and music, which contain the images of acts superbly performed. When the arts digress so far from reality that their symbolism is comprehensible only to a few who have been indoctrinated, the lives of the rest are deprived of a source of satisfaction. This deprivation may even result in depression and profound discontent.

If the suicide rate of a culture is an index of the extent of its discontent, then it is greatest in some of the most highly developed societies. In the United States, it is the fifth leading cause of death among persons between the ages of fifteen and fifty, whereas in more primitive societies suicide is nearly nonexistent. Among animals in their natural uncrowded state, suicide does not occur. It is only when an animal is made captive that it will sometimes destroy itself. Perhaps in certain human societies man has been made captive by his own customs. Perhaps he has become so contained by his symbolism that the reality of life, with its pleasures and pain, has become meaningless.

The fundamental delights of life, in food and drink, in work and play, in love and beauty, are natural to man. His troubles are largely of his own making, built up in a complicated structure of symbols and words. Failure in business does not mean that the one who has experienced it will be deprived of food or drink or shelter. The loss of a beloved one does not imply that the bereaved will be forever denied love. It is the symbolism of the words men use to express their failures or losses which is so distressing to them. They forget that the pleasures of the senses are inherent and cannot be taken from them, except in serious illnesses.

It is possible that some children are harmed by the deadly competition for admission to college. It has been reported that 16.2 per cent of the students entering a men's liberal arts college in the class of 1967 showed "clinically significant emotional impairment," and that its incidence was more than twice as high as it had been five years before. The increased prevalence of emotional impairment ran parallel to an increase in the academic potential of the students in these classes as measured by scholastic aptitude tests. Of the emotionally impaired students with high verbal aptitudes, 31.8 per cent withdrew from college. Their failures were attributed to inadequate capacities to attain independence, interpersonal relationships, and real pleasure.

J. G. Gray, professor of philosophy at Colorado College, says that students today are concerned with their individual and personal experience in an age that threatens to overwhelm individuality. But how can the student attain individuality? To gain admission to a university, he must pass the same required courses as every other student; then for the first year or two, he is obliged to study the same subjects that they do. Finally, when the time comes to select the courses he wants, the student finds that each is a part of a rigid discipline, not well adapted to his interests or needs, unless he is going to specialize in that field. The courses are often so packed with detail to be memorized that they dampen instead of stimulate his interest. In short, it is not learning that is made the student's goal, but the degree. As John Dewey said, "The center of gravity is outside the child. It is the teacher, the textbook, anywhere and everywhere you please except in the immediate instincts and activities of the child himself."

The long and grinding competition for high marks, extending through high school, college, and even into graduate schools, may contribute to a person's inability to find contentment. A child, brought up to believe that the struggle for grades is the key to success in life and carrying that belief on through graduate school, may be unable to enjoy success even if he attains it. The competition has become an end in itself. He has worked so steadily all his life that he rejects all values which do not pertain to his work.

Although rejection of values operates at a psychological level, it can be as complete and irreversible as is the rejection of sight in the type of blindness called amblyopia of disuse. This is a form of blindness that occurs in one eye of a cross-eyed child. To avoid perceiving a double image, the child unconsciously rejects the visual images from one or the other eye. Unless the dominant eye is patched promptly to force use of the suppressed one, all useful vision of the rejected eye will be permanently lost. In much the same way a person who has worked too hard and too long may become so blind to other pleasures that he feels lost when retirement suddenly alters his lifelong habits of thought and action.

From the standpoint of obtaining happiness it might be rewarding to apply to education what already has been discovered about the process of learning and the development of the human mind. If we did this, we might become more interested in the quality of life than in its length, more concerned with what we feel and enjoy than with the technology of production. If this should come to pass, it will not be by extending college or postgraduate education but by applying what is already known to the rearing of the infant and the child.

If there is a flock of a dozen hens, they work out a ladder of dominance in the pecking order and none of the hens is neurotic. There must be among men, in common with other creatures, natural followers as well as leaders. It may be unkind to attempt to rear children always to a strong sense of competition and a desire for superiority. If instead of fighting their way through life, they could be reared to look for simple ways to enjoy it, people might find more contentment. There is an old saying: Success is getting what you want and happiness is wanting what you get.

CHAPTER SEVEN

Sexuality

There is hardly any aspect of the behavior of animals which may not have some reference to problems in human behavior.
—William H. Thorpe

As I talk with patients, observe friends, and think back over my own experiences, it seems to me that successful and lasting marriages depend less on the sexual drive and competence of the partners than on their ability to establish and maintain affectionate and tolerant interpersonal relationships. Regardless of how passionately they are attracted to one another physically, that attraction can be destroyed by intolerance, nagging, and lack of consideration. These traits, it seems to me, are most apt to develop in the perfectionists of the world, those with set ways that they consider to be indisputably correct. I have often wondered whether the development of this type of personality is not encouraged by such things as giving a child a room of his own instead of having him share a room with someone so that he will learn to be adaptable to the ways of others.

Although the stability of a marriage may depend chiefly on the ability of the partners to adjust to one another and live together in harmony, it is usually sexual attraction that first brings them together. In the human being, the sex drive is not seasonal, as with most other creatures. It is present all year round, captivating man's interest, sometimes obsessing his thoughts. If mankind had not developed this strong interest in sex, perhaps the race might not have survived, for the period of human gestation is long, multiple births are few, and the difficulties in rearing the young are many. It seems unlikely, however, that sex evolved primarily for the purpose of reproduction. The method is too inefficient. The complexities of successfully fertilizing an egg cell are so great that most eggs die with their potential unfulfilled. If nature had wanted the human being to reproduce in the most efficient way, it would be asexually, like the daisy.

Every daisy, as well as every aster and dandelion, is a composite flower and the product of a virgin birth. The daisy's far-off ancestors reproduced by cross-pollination, and therefore the plant still has flowers. But as the daisy evolved, it gradually froze into its present form in which it does not depend for the future upon the wind or insects or birds or even on a male and female organ within itself. No sexual process takes place, yet the fields are covered with the successful and efficient daisies.

Because there is no interaction of genetic material between daisies, the possibility of a mutation is slight. The species has no "genetic pool" of mutations to call upon in case of a disastrous change in environment. It will be less able to adapt to whatever changes may occur in the future than will many sexual plants which are not so successful today. It seems that while sex is not the most efficient way of reproduction, it affords a kind of insurance by which mutation and adaptation are assured.

In both human beings and animals, sexual development and motivation depend largely upon the presence of sex hormones. Thus if a mother carrying a female embryo is given an excess of a masculinizing hormone, the child may be masculinized and born a hermaphrodite with external genitalia resembling a male's. Similarly when a cow has twins, one male and the other female, the female one is exposed to the male hormone that her brother makes and grows up to be a sterile freemartin.

The effect of the sex hormones is not limited to embryonic life. If they are given medically to adults they stimulate or inhibit the types of cells which respond to them. Estrogen can so stimulate the growth of a man's breasts that they become indistinguishable from a woman's. Conversely, the masculinizing androgens, given to a female, make the breasts shrink and cause growth of facial hair and clitoris.

The brain as well as the body responds to the presence of sex hormones. If doses of them, far too small to have any effect on the genital organs, are injected into a certain part of a rat's brain, the appropriate male or female sex behavior will be evoked. Perfect male mating patterns were induced in females by treating them in this way with male hormones, illustrating that the females are equipped with both male and female mechanisms of sex response.

The brain cells that regulate sexual behavior lie dormant unless the proper hormone stimulates them. If a male dog is castrated before he is sexually mature, he will not chase or mount females and seldom lifts his leg to urinate. If a man is castrated before puberty, the male type of sex behavior will not evolve.

The development of the sex drive does not depend so much on age as on the presence of the proper hormones in large enough amounts to stimulate the brain cells. I have had a four-year-old boy patient with a tumor that made an excess of male hormone, who had pubic hair and fully developed genitalia. He showed sex behavior characteristic of puberty, masturbating and making exploratory sex advances. At the other extreme, women, even in their seventies and eighties, may experience sharp revivals of sexual appetites when they receive androgens in the treatment of cancer of the breast.

Once the response of the brain cells has been established by the sex hormones, the process is apt to be irreversible. An adult sexually experienced man does not necessarily lose his potency if castrated, nor does he develop a female type of sex behavior if given estrogens. Behavior, in adult life, is firmly fixed and difficult to alter.

Experiences encountered early in life may have as profound an effect upon later sexual behavior as do the sex hormones. A hand-reared male turkey is apt to disregard turkey hens, display to the person he is imprinted on, and try to copulate with some symbol of him, like a shoe. A young gander, imprinted on one of our fallow deer, followed her about all day long, grooming her ears and face, and gabbling to her. On two separate occasions we had a buck rabbit, taken early from his mother and reared with chickens, who mated with a bantam hen, copulating effectively. In one case the hen decided to set, and we took the eggs she laid and replaced them with fertile ones. When they hatched, the rabbit helped the hen raise the chicks, who perched on his back and nestled in his fur.

In nature, animals or birds of different species usually disregard one another sexually. As long ago as 1908, however, two species of wild pigeons were successfully crossed by rearing the young of one species with adults of the other. This method has become a standard device among bird breeders, widely used to promote interbreeding of species. Another way of accomplishing interspecies crosses is to rear the young together, as zoo keepers do when they cross lions and tigers and produce "tiglons." One can conjecture in this vein as to whether the great mixing of white and black races, which occurred in the South during the days of slavery, was motivated in part by the employment of Negro women as nurses for the children of the whites.

Sexual behavior is affected not only by the experiences that are encountered in early life, but by the deprivations also. Male chimpanzees, reared to maturity without females, often are unable to copulate successfully even with receptive females. At the University of Wisconsin, the Harlows have done experiments on monkeys that seem to relate to human beings. They took two groups of infant monkeys away from their mothers at birth and reared each infant with an artificial mother, a model with a milk bottle protruding from its chest. In the first group, each baby was isolated with its surrogate mother and not allowed to play with other monkeys. Those of the second group were free to play with each other and indulge in normal inter-infant relationships. The monkeys who were reared in solitude grew up unable to engage in normal social activities. They cowered in corners or suddenly attacked one another. Few were interested in sex activity. The young monkeys in the group who were allowed to play with each other, however, developed normal social and sexual patterns of behavior. There is an analogy between this experiment and the one in which chimpanzees, reared without sticks to play with, were unable later on to learn to use them as tools. The Harlows' monkeys, having grown up without monkeys to play with, simply could not relate to other monkeys. Occasionally some of the female monkeys in the experiments, who had been reared alone, became pregnant and bore young. However, they never cared for them properly. One or two "struck their babies, bit them, crushed them to the floor, and jumped on them without any apparent provocation." This behavior brings to mind the stories of "battered children" mistreated by their parents and so luridly reported in newspapers of late.

At the time of puberty, most normal male animals, including the human, exhibit homosexual behavior of an exploratory type. These tendencies are replaced soon by heterosexual activities. But if the parent protects his child too strictly from sex play, or if the child is overly fearful of the possible consequences of a heterosexual relationship, sex development may become arrested at the homosexual level. The pattern can become fixed and difficult to alter. It is believed that this type of arrested development is responsible for most homosexual behavior, and especially the common type, where there is no overt mannerism to denote the tendency. This may also account for the prevalence of homosexual practice in many of the countries where intimate premarital association between sexes is banned and marriages are made late. Bestiality, a form of human sexuality that is directed toward animals, is alleged to be common among men who have been reared from childhood in the isolated occupation of tending sheep or llamas. In these circumstances, the practice seems to be not so much a perversion as an adaptation to being deprived of human contact.

There may be a type of homosexual whose traits have been transmitted genetically or caused by abnormal conditions before birth. According to Dr. Walter Alvarez, many mothers of male homosexuals say that the boy behaved like a girl before he was three years old. In many of these there are feminine mannerisms and traits. Perhaps this type of homosexual was exposed, during embryonic life, to an excess of sex hormone that overstimulated a sexual center of the brain. A genetic abnormality is also possible, for there is a parasitic wasp that occasionally produces a gynandromorph, having the sex organs of one sex and the brain of the other, as shown by a study of the chromosomes. It has a male head, female reproductive organs, and courts females. Although it is possible that similar aberrations occur in humans, there is as yet no proof of it. All that can be said is that regardless of its cause homosexual behavior usually is irreversible. Punishment is not an effective deterrent. Re-education is difficult, if not impossible. When the homosexual practice is once established in an adult man or woman, the pattern of behavior appears to be fixed.

The drive of sex is often associated with the emotion of love. Sometimes, in human beings it is mistaken for it. In nature, the sexual urge and love may blend so that they become almost indistinguishable, as in the case of geese and swans, which are monogamous and usually mate for life. However, in most species, sexual activity is not accompanied by loving-type behavior. If it is, this behavior may not include sexual fidelity.

The ringneck doves in our flight cage hatch and rear successions of babies. The oldest male bird always nests with his established mate. When their female chicks are nearly grown, the father occasionally copulates with them, but he never deserts his mate. He continues to groom her, copulate with her, bring her straw for their nest, and sets on the eggs alternately with her. When he breeds the young females, he is responding to the drive of sex, but he separates it from his responsibility to his mate and their nest. One is reminded of the adventures of Captain Cook in his visit to Tahiti, where the Polynesians thought the younger generation ought to be fully trained in sexual matters as quickly as possible and the older generation "took care that they should obtain guidance as soon as they began to be sexually mature."

The reproductive behavior of ringneck doves has been studied under controlled conditions. Although the female will not build a nest unless the male is close by, she does not depend solely on the act of copulation to evoke egg laying. Development of the ovary is stimulated by the sight and sound of the male, although he may be separated from her by a pane of glass. The same is true of the male dove; the crop glands with which he makes "milk" for the young develop rapidly if he sees his mate setting on the nest through the glass. The attraction of each bird to one of the opposite sex also evokes the instinct to cooperate in building the nest and feeding the young.

In birds and human beings, it is often the sex drive that brings the couples together and sets the stage for the development of the type of behavior that is characteristic of love. However, nature has no fixed rules for accomplishing her ends. In contrast to the doves, Canada geese fall in love before they are sexually mature. Although they do not copulate until their second year, they will often take a mate in their first, and remain faithful for life. In certain human societies also, it has been arranged for children to marry before they are able to consummate the ceremony. Often too, it has been the custom for a marriage to be settled between a young man and woman who have never before met. Since these arrangements often worked well it seems that there are many ways to evoke loving behavior and that sex attraction is only one of them. Another, and a more binding one, is the mutual dependence of the partners on one another in playing their role as a couple in the life of the family, the community, and the home.

In view of the diversity of the arrangements that both men and animals have devised for regulating their sexual behavior the question arises as to whether conventional standards of sex morality are anachronistic in a time when venereal diseases are rare, when serious consequences no longer arise as a result of contracting them, and when conception can be prevented at will. Without denying the value and satisfactions of sexual union in marriage, the issue is whether or not marriages would be more stable and satisfactory if it were the accepted custom to have premarital sex experiences and less rigid rules of intramarital behavior.

If there were a single standard of sexual morality that was best adapted to the rearing of babies and the education of children, one would suppose that through the centuries it would have been of survival value and would have replaced all others. In the present Western culture, monogamy, premarital continence, and marital fidelity have been viewed as the foundations of sexual morality. Yet in Scotland, only a century and a half ago, when the warring clans were solid family groups, trial marriages were regular occurrences. If the union was not satisfactory, the couple parted and the children were adopted by the clan. Modern Sweden may be returning to old customs. It is reported that nowadays nearly half of the first-born children there are conceived before marriage takes place. In Denmark a new law authorizes any fifteen to eighteen-year-old girl to go to a physician or clinic for contraceptive advice or material.

In the Middle East and the Orient, polygamy was widely practiced, and in some areas still is. Certain women, like the geishas of Japan, in spite of their usually having had premarital experience, were not looked down upon as prospective wives. In some of the Polynesian islands, a woman was not considered a candidate for marriage until she had proved herself fertile. In other areas, polyandry was the custom, and in still others, as is said to have been true of the legendary Amazons, men were not tolerated except at certain seasons. In some cultures, notably the Eskimos', unmarried women and even wives were freely lent to visitors.

In viewing the various solutions which societies have made to the problems of sex, one is reminded of certain diseases about whose treatment there is interminable debate. As long as the arguments continue, one can be quite sure that either all of the treatments are equally effective, or none are effective at all. Since sexual relations no longer need result in pregnancy, it may be that the manner in which they are conducted will become a matter of individual taste.

"Beware of moral principles," Edmund Leach, anthropologist at Cambridge University, has said. "A zeal to do right leads to the segregation of sinners, and the sinners can then be shut away out of sight and subjected to violence. Other creatures and other people besides ourselves have a right to exist and we must somehow or other try to see where they fit in. . . . So long as we allow our perceptions to be guided by morality," Leach continues, "we shall see evil when there is none." The unfortunate thing is that we are seldom able to see facts as they are.

The facts are that sexual activity affords great pleasure to human beings and is essential to the future of their race. It seems sad, then, that our Western culture has developed such stern rules for its conduct. In an era when sexual relations no longer need result in pregnancy or disease, it seems cruel to teach continence to adolescents whose sexual drives are at their peaks and to punish those who do not comply. Existing moral values are not the measure by which the rightness or wrongness of sexual behavior should be appraised. It is the moral values themselves that should be reassessed.

Regardless of how our Western culture's code of morality may change, as long as the family group persists, man and woman will continue to live together in the state of mutual interdependency that we call love. Since the sexual urge is as necessary to the continuity of the human race as the spur of hunger is to the survival of the individual, mankind will continue to be intrigued with the subject of sex. From the lyrics of Sappho in 600 B.C. to present-day literature, human beings have done their best to describe the emotions of sexual love in all their variations. In the most widely read book in the Western hemisphere, Solomon's Song of Songs begins: "Let him kiss me with the kisses of his mouth: for thy love is better than wine."

CHAPTER EIGHT

Health and Superstition

I think I could turn and live with the
animals, they are so placid and self-
contained,
I stand and look at them long and long.
They do not sweat and whine about their
condition,
They do not lie awake in the dark and
weep for their sins,
They do not make me sick discussing
their duty to God.
Not one is dissatisfied, not one is de-
mented with the mania of owning
things,
Not one kneels to another, nor to his kind
that lived thousands of years ago,
Not one is responsible or unhappy over
the whole earth.
            —Walt Whitman, "Song of Myself"

My father, who was a surgeon and a biological philosopher, was not atheistic in the sense in which the word is sometimes used to denote antagonism to the concept of God. His philosophy could better be described as naturalistic. It tried to explain as much of nature as possible without resorting to the supernatural and it assumed that what could not yet be explained might ultimately be, along scientific lines. However, at times we children had experiences that made us wonder.

One night our family was sitting on the edge of the cliff in the forest of our country place. A tremendous electrical storm was sweeping toward us from Lake Erie. All of us were watching the lightning strike closer and closer, like a creeping barrage of artillery fire. After a particularly loud crash, my father shook his fist at the heavens.

"I defy you to hit us!" he shouted.

At that moment the lightning struck an oak tree ten feet from us, splitting it in two and ripping off pieces of bark. There was silence and the scent of ozone in the air.

At that moment I had an inkling of how belief in the power of the supernatural began.

As science developed, the figure of Zeus, hurling his thunderbolts, began to be replaced by the concept of static electricity. Science has gone far in the interpretation of the world, but since the mysteries of the universe appear to be infinite, it is unlikely that man, a finite being, will ever be able to understand all of it.

Nor is he able to explain his own consciousness, his feeling of individuality, and the mysteries of his own life and death.

Although we know little of the religions of prehistoric man, we do have knowledge of some of the beliefs, like Christianity, which have arisen in recorded times. We know that at their beginnings, it was not demanded that man be persecuted, tortured, or killed, as happened in the Middle Ages, to sustain the glory of a god. The original prophets did not teach this; it was the result of customs which through the centuries evolved in the cults of followers.

If a belief is instilled in a child before he develops the ability to criticize or reason, the child is likely to be imprinted with it so strongly that it becomes a part of his personality. Each new generation accepts the premises transmitted to it from the one before, embellishes them, and transmits them in turn to the next. Finally the beliefs, whether clerical, demanding abstinence and sacrifice, or medical, involving the supposed values of bleeding, purging, and certain more modern practices, become harmful rather than helpful. Before what happened is generally recognized, much damage has been done.

At the turn of the last century, anesthesia and control of infection had developed to the point where surgical operations were relatively safe. The next step was that they became stylish. During this period more and more patients were diagnosed as having appendicitis and were operated upon. Some people developed such a fear of appendicitis that, even though they had no symptoms of it, they demanded to have their appendixes removed to keep them from getting the disease. The death rate attributed to appendicitis and the treatment of supposed appendicitis rose from 9.7 per cent for every 100,000 in 1900, to 13.4 per cent in 1920, and to 15.3 per cent in 1930. At that time the American College of Surgeons began to establish tissue committees in hospitals to determine whether too many normal appendixes were being removed. After this the death rate stabilized. It was not, however, until sulfanilamide and later the antibiotics became available that the death rate fell rapidly to 1.7 per cent.

The history of appendicitis is an example of overtreatment causing loss of more lives from complications of unnecessary treatments than were saved by necessary ones. Because physicians who did not overtreat their patients were often considered to be disinterested or careless and those who overtreated, even to the point of loss of life, were generally regarded as having tried to do everything that was humanly possible, the blame for this situation must be shared by the physicians and the laity alike.

Although today's children hear little about the fire and brimstone of the afterworld, their mothers and teachers seem set upon indoctrinating them with the concept of the horrors of disease. A lifetime pattern of concern or even of hypochondria can be induced in this way. Knowledge about disease contributes little to the welfare of a young child and much to his subsequent anxiety about health. The cathartic habit, started in a child by an overanxious mother, can persist for a lifetime.

The physician may also be to blame for his patients' overconcern about their health. If he is oversolicitous and puts a young girl with a stomach ache of emotional origin into the hospital, or if, in the absence of clear signs, he operates on her to rule out the possibility of appendicitis, the behavior pattern of hypochrondria may be initiated. By the time the patient is a woman of forty, she may have had six or eight additional abdominal operations; first on an ovary, then a hysterectomy, then more for supposed obstructions of the bowel or for adhesions. This type of behavior is obviously not intrinsic to the human being; it is the result of early training. Neuroses instilled into children by false medical beliefs can cause as great a deviation from reality as did the religious beliefs which led the early Christians to plead with the Romans to torture and martyr them.

One of the problems in the treatment of disease is that the physician is not primarily a scientist. He is a practitioner. He desires to cure his patient and also to satisfy him. If the patient does not need treatment, but is convinced he does, the physician may prescribe something simply to please. This can establish in the patient a pattern of dependence. The nostrums, vitamins, and worthless remedies which are so widely advertised and sold over drugstore counters, as well as the vitamin B_{12} or hormone shots so frequently given by the physicians without proper indications, demonstrate the strong desire that patients have for treatment with no regard for its intrinsic worth. It has been said that patients prefer a bit of humble attention to the most distinguished neglect.

If medicine did not have side effects, if operations did not have complications which were sometimes fatal, and if diagnostic tests and treatments did not result occasionally in serious complications, these measures might be used for their psychotherapeutic value. Unfortunately they involve dangers. It is estimated that 10 to 15 per cent of patients in general hospitals are there because of the side effects of treatment. Hospitalization itself involves the risk of both accident and contagion. Re-education of the patient is safer than overdiagnosis or overtreatment done to allay anxiety. The assumption that the most treatment is the best treatment is both dangerous and false. So is the assumption that the newest type of treatment is always the best.

A physician may persuasively report a theory about a disease or a new treatment which he thought was successful. His enthusiasm, or a chance success, may lead to overacceptance of the method before it is critically evaluated. So great is the psychological effect of the new treatment upon physician and patient alike that its results cannot be accurately assayed unless evaluated scientifically. This can be accomplished only by a randomized experiment in which neither physician nor patient knows whether the treatment on trial has been given or withheld. Without this critical evaluation, worthless or even dangerous remedies will continue to sweep the country.

A recent example of overtreatment is the prolonged use of the anticoagulants that for more than twenty years were almost universally given to prevent further clotting of blood in patients who had had the coronary arteries of their hearts blocked by blood clots. Although dangerous hemorrhages sometimes resulted from use of the anticoagulants, so reasonable did the theory sound that it went unchallenged until recent controlled studies in Scandinavia and elsewhere proved that the long-term use of anticoagulants is of no value.

Medical styles sometimes seem like religious cults, endorsed by the one who administers and accepted with faith by the one who receives. In the seventeenth century, the English believed that scrofula, a tuberculous infection of the lymph nodes, could be cured by the king's touch. Charles II was said to have touched 100,000 of the scrofulous people who came to him in great throngs. Public experiments could not shake this belief, which survived even the Reformation.

The history of both medicine and religion shows that what people see in life is chiefly what they expect to see, or what they wish to see. Once, in a hospital in which I worked, a patient was sent to the obstetrical department by an intern who said the woman was giving birth to her baby through the rectum, an extraordinarily rare but possible complication in women with injuries or deformities of the parts. So strong was the power of suggestion that in the delivery room all the physicians involved averred they felt the "sutures" and the "soft spot" of the baby's head and when the "head" appeared, someone remarked that it had black hair. The "baby" of course proved to be a giant impaction of stool. Bernard Shaw once remarked, "The moment we want to stop believing in anything we have hitherto believed in, we not only find that there are many objections to it, but also that these objections have been staring us in the face all the time."

Mankind does not seem to learn easily from past mistakes. Gibbon has estimated that two thousand Christian martyrs were killed during the Diocletian persecution. From this carnage, the survivors derived no distaste for persecution, and generations later, they, in turn, established the Spanish Inquisition. During the presidency of Torquemada alone the descendants of the martyred Christians burned approximately the same number of heretics.

Religious massacres and the suppression of idolatry by force were supposed, by the people of the time, to be approved of and enjoined by the deity. Although today those who perpetrated them are viewed as cruel and sadistic, it is probable that the persecutors considered themselves to be benefactors of mankind. They were attempting to help their victims by protecting them from the damnation which was understood to be in store for them as a result of their beliefs.

With sincerity equal to that of the inquisitors, nineteenth-century doctors purged and bled their patients, often already anemic or in shock, to rid them of supposed poisons. No estimate has been made of the number of deaths caused by those practices. Voltaire, who lived during the height of them, wrote, "Doctors pour drugs of which they know little, to cure diseases of which they know less, into human beings of whom they know nothing." Physicians today, in respect to the treatment of some diseases, are in the same situation. Drugs are more dangerous than ever, and the list is growing of new diseases which arise from their use. Yet when patients hear of the new remedies, they insist upon trying them before their safety has been established.

Some physicians, not scientifically oriented, appear to be much like members of a priesthood in their persistence in the rituals of their practice. Their patients often seek out these mystic rites, involving weekly hormone shots or unnecessary hysterectomies. The physicians and surgeons, motivated by their patients' demands, may develop practices as pernicious as some of the religious rites of the Middle Ages. Already in the treatment of certain types of cancer, this seems to have come about.

The central problem in both medicine and religion is to keep the practitioners as free as possible of dogma. In the case of religion, this implies a close adherence to pure spiritual beliefs; in the case of medicine, to science. This is not always easy because a private practitioner of medicine depends for his living on "fee for service" and hence on the necessity of pleasing his patients. The patient, if not satisfied with the type of care given by one physician, can seek another. It is not always the most scientific type of treatment that he chooses.

There is a tendency for human beings to feel that their life spans can be extended. Although man cannot conceive of infinite time or space, he has often sought eternal life. It is not easy for him to comprehend his own death. It is difficult for him to think of the universe without himself in it, for his concept of the universe is merely the record of his individual education and experience. Perhaps this is why so many religious creeds have promised an afterworld. It may explain why, now, when belief in the hereafter is fading, man wants to postpone the hour of his death. The huge temples of past ages, dedicated to the concept of eternal life, may have their modern counterparts in the gigantic and ever-growing hospitals. In the days of the pharaohs, the pyramids were erected; in the Middle Ages cathedrals towered over the towns; today hospitals seem on their way to becoming the largest edifices of our nation.

It is possible that if children are brought up to have too firm a faith in the miracles of modern medicine, they may disregard facts. One of these is that medical treatment can do little to prolong the lives of older people. Since the turn of the century there has been an enormous improvement in the life expectancy of a baby at birth, but this is due almost entirely to control of infant mortality and infectious disease. In 1910, the further life expectancy of a man at the age of sixty-five was 11.5 years. In 1962, it was 12.9 years. This is an improvement of only 1.4 years in over half a century. Most of this gain is attributable to antibiotic control of acute infections like pneumonia rather than to success in the treatment of chronic or degenerative diseases of the aged.

Nobel Laureate Sir Macfarlane Burnet recently pointed out that no one has found a way of persuading people to stop cigarette smoking, overeating, or fast driving, which are the main causes of the increasing incidence of unnecessary deaths today. It seems that until there is a way of making every child and adolescent understand the elements of human biology and its bearing on life in a scientifically oriented society, there is little hope of a healthy and peaceful world.

It is not generally recognized that even if all disease could be prevented or cured people still would not live much longer than they do now, for death is not necessarily due to disease or injury. A katydid dies with the coming of winter, even when it is kept in a greenhouse, warm and well fed. The span of life of all the higher animals is finite; this is true even of the tissues and organs of which they are composed. If human cells are put in tissue culture they will not live and reproduce themselves indefinitely. There appears to be a limit to the number of times that a cell from a specialized tissue can divide—about fifty, if the cell comes from an embryo, and only about half as many if it comes from an old person. After that the cells stop dividing and die.

If cells from an embryo are mixed with those from an adult, all the adult cells will stop dividing and die before those of the embryo do. There are left only the cells from the embryo, which can be distinguished by their chromosomes if the embryo from which the cells came was of a different sex than the adult.

It is not only in tissue culture that cells have a fixed span of life. When ovaries taken from an old mouse are transplanted into a young one of the same inbred strain, the young mouse rarely gets pregnant. This holds true also when ovaries from a young mouse are transplanted into an old one. It is only when the ovaries from a young mouse are transplanted into another young mouse that pregnancy will ensue. It has been found also that when skin is taken from an old mouse and transplanted onto a young one, it cannot sustain itself for long the way skin from a young mouse does. It gradually withers and becomes replaced. The three-score-and-ten estimate of the average span of man's life is as valid today as in the days of the Prophets, for the ganglion cells of the nervous system and brain cannot reproduce themselves and die off, one by one, from middle age on, even in the absence of recognized disease.

Of the deaths due to heart disease, 72 per cent occur after the age of sixty-five, as well as 55 per cent of those attributable to cancer, and 80 per cent of those due to stroke. If most of the people affected did not die of these diseases, they soon would of something else. For most of them no highly effective treatment is yet known. England and Sweden have well-organized state medical systems in which patients with cancer or stroke are more apt to be cared for by well-trained specialists in specialized hospitals than here in America. Nevertheless they have not obtained higher rates of survival. If progress in the treatment of cancer is measured by the age-adjusted survival rate per 100,-000 people, there has been little or no improvement in any country in the last fifty years.

For some types of cancer, such as those of the cervix and stomach, the death rate has decreased. In the case of the cervix, this is due to better methods of early diagnosis, and of the stomach, because for some unknown reason the disease in Western countries has become less common. In lung cancer, both the incidence and the death rate have increased, as a result of cigarette smoking. In most types of cancer, like that of the breast, the incidence and death rates have remained the same. It would seem that heavy expenditures in research into the causes and treatments of diseases are justified. However, it remains questionable whether it is wise to build vast facilities to treat diseases in elaborate ways when no highly effective means of treating them is known.

In the treatment of heart disease there seems to be promise for the future. It is possible to control much of the high blood pressure that so often results in failure of the heart. Valves that are diseased or defective can be replaced. When there is blockage of a coronary artery, blood can be returned to the deprived heart muscle, either by removing the obstruction in the artery or by transplanting a new one into the heart. Many lives might be prolonged if there were more special centers equipped with the complex facilities and special skills required to diagnose and treat heart disease. Yet to date, there has been no scientific study to evaluate the results of these new techniques. Before there can be widespread application of any new methods there must be investigation and open discussion of them by the scientific community. Dr. Irvine H. Page, past president of the American Heart Society, has said, "Too often science is regarded only as a means of satisfying immediate social demands, and such demands sometimes produce pressure which erode the integrity of science." Thus man's dreams of eternal life should not lead him to attempt the impossible.

Through the centuries there have been many philosophies regarding the acceptance of death. Spinoza wrote, "There is no subject on which the sage will think less than death." The Stoic philosophers believed that death not only followed but preceded life. They said, "It is to be as we were before we were born. The candle which has been extinguished is in the same condition as before it was lit, and the dead man as the man unborn . . . It is at worst but the close of a banquet we have enjoyed." The Augustinian doctrine was

quite different and conferred damnation on the un-
baptized, even if they were infants. Perhaps in the
Western world, a lingering belief in the latter dogma
plays a part in man's fear of death.

One of the physician's duties is to help his patients
face their end without fear. This is not impossible, for
dying itself is rarely hard. It is the fear of it which
makes it so and robs the frightened one of many of the
pleasures he might enjoy in his remaining time.
Montaigne, centuries ago, said, "The Thing I am Most
afraid of is, Fear, because it is a Passion which super-
sedes and suspends all others . . . Fear is even more
vexatious and insupportable than Death."

Illness and injury, in proportion to their severity,
numb the senses and dull the pain. Twice I have come
near to death, once in the twenties, before sulfanilamide or antibiotics, when I had a near-fatal pneumonia, and again recently, after an automobile accident
in which I suffered nine broken ribs and a ruptured
spleen. I have no recollections, during the crises of
these occasions, of either fear or pain. There was only
a drowsy and impersonal acceptance of the situation.

I have seldom seen a patient who seemed to be suffering as death approached. Euthanasia, a method of
causing death painlessly to end the suffering of patients
with incurable disease, is advocated by people who
view the suffering not as the patient does, sick and with
senses dulled by apathy, but as they, in their full vigor,
fancy they would interpret it. In a sense it is because
the witnesses are so involved that they wish the scene

to be quickly ended. I have observed the same situation when pets were deformed by some accident or disease. Their masters insisted on putting an end to a suffering which existed not in their animals but in their empathy with them. And in respect to illness in human beings there always remains the possibility that a cure may be discovered tomorrow.

Regardless of how close death seems to be, one still cannot disregard the pleasures of the moment. Patients with psychological depressions may become suicidal, but those with diseases of the body do not ask to be put to death. They are either too sick to be aware or too engaged in the events of a novel way of living. One of my patients, an energetic woman with an incurable cancer, told me, "I'm not afraid to die. It's just that I'm so busy I don't have time for it."

The Western world puts great stress upon the life of the individual. In St. Matthew, Jesus asks, "How think ye? If a man have a hundred sheep, and one of them be gone astray, doth he not leave the ninety and nine, and goeth into the mountains, and seeketh that which is gone astray?" This principle, applied to treatment, can make it difficult for either the patient or his physician to accept the fact there are diseases in which there is a better expectancy for a longer and more comfortable life if the physician does not treat each patient radically, as the one sheep, in the hope of a cure. An example would be a patient beyond the age of sixty, with the common type of cancer of the pancreas.

If the patient is told that his only chance of cure of

pancreatic cancer is a dangerous and disabling operation, he is apt to accept the proposed treatment. What
he does not realize is that at this age, cure does not
mean "saving" his life, only extending it a little. The
value of a treatment should be appraised not in terms of
cure, but in terms of the months or years of useful life
that can be expected if it is given. In patients sixty or
seventy years old with cancers of the pancreas, the
average span of life will be longer if all are subjected
to a relatively simple operation to relieve the symptoms without removing the tumor than if all were
treated by a radical one designed to cure. The radical
operation is so ineffective that only 1 or 2 per cent are
cured by it, with the result that the years gained by
these few are not enough to compensate for those lost
by the many who die as the immediate result of the
operation. The trouble is that those who die forfeit
the months of pleasant living they might have enjoyed
if they had not tried to be cured. Some patients, after
simple operations in which the cancer is not even removed, live as long as five years.

Ways are now being developed to transplant organs
—kidneys, hearts, livers, and lungs. When these
methods have been perfected, problems connected with
prolongation of life are going to be greatly multiplied.
Already they are beginning to arise, not only in respect
to who should receive an organ, but also as to when it
is permissible to take a vital organ from a donor. The
latter point is of supreme importance, for if the organ
is not transplanted soon after the donor's death its cells

die and it is useless. The problem is to define death, a task that is not always easy, as illustrated by a recent experience in a Cleveland hospital.

The patient was a man in his mid-forties who was in the recovery room following an operation in which a new valve had been put into his failing heart. All went well for three hours, but then the rhythm of the pulse became irregular and circulation began to fail.

The patient was operated on again, to make sure that there had been no technical complications. Everything was found to be in order. The heart continued to fail, the disturbances in rhythm became uncontrollable, and finally the heart stopped. Efforts to revive it did not succeed.

Attempts to resuscitate the patient by massaging the heart were continued for an hour, during which time the electrocardiogram showed no flicker of activity in the motionless heart muscle. The patient was pronounced dead.

In the same hospital, a young man with kidney failure was being kept alive by treatment with an artificial kidney in hopes that a healthy kidney would become available for transplantation. As soon as the heart patient was pronounced dead, the doctors in charge of the kidney patient were notified. In the meantime, artificial respiration and cardiac massage were continued, not in any hope of restoring the dead man's life but in order to maintain circulation in the kidney and keep it alive until permission to transplant it could be obtained.

The widow of the heart patient, having been assured that everything was going well, had left the hospital before her husband's unexpected complication occurred and was nowhere to be found. For four hours, while the search for her continued, the young residents strove to keep the kidneys alive by massaging the heart and aerating the lungs. During this time the monitoring electrocardiogram showed no activity in the heart.

At this point, a resident ran into the room carrying a slip, signed by the widow, granting permission to transplant the kidneys. At this point also the electrocardiogram showed a heartbeat. Within a minute the heart was beating normally. Ten minutes later the patient awoke and began to speak. He is still living and well.

The irony is that the effort which saved the patient was not inspired by any hope of reviving him but by trying to save his kidney so another man could live. What had happened was that after the first operation some chemical disturbance in the blood had made it temporarily impossible for the heart to beat. With the passage of time the artificially maintained circulation corrected the imbalance and the heart was again able to function.

The transplantation of organs is at present an extremely costly procedure, and its long-range benefit has not as yet been established. As more and more teams become trained and competent in transplanting kidneys, hearts, livers, and lungs, society will be faced with the question of how much it can afford to spend to keep one of its members alive. This responsibility will have to be accurately defined. When transplantation of organs becomes practicable and if facilities for it are limited, the future man may have to rear his children in a type of philosophy based not on hopes of eternal life but on what the chances are of prolonging a pleasant and useful life. Acceptance of the decisions that must be made will involve the development of a philosophy about death.

Although animals are conscious, it is man alone among them who possesses a mirror that reflects his consciousness and makes him aware of his own individuality and of his life and his death. Animals do not appear to be aware of death as it applies to themselves. They fear death-dealing agents, but not the experience of dying. If an animal is mortally ill, he simply wanders off quietly and alone.

In the human, it is death itself which causes the greatest terror. If children could be reared to make no unnatural mystery of the event, they might look without fear into the unexplored infinities of space and time. It was the Preacher in Ecclesiastes who said, "A man should rejoice in his own works; for who shall bring him to see what shall be after him."

CHAPTER NINE

The Organization of Society

Now this is the Law of the Jungle—as old
*   and as true as the sky;*
And the Wolf that shall keep it may pros-
*   per, but the Wolf that shall break*
*   it must die.*

As the creeper that girdles the tree-trunk
*   the Law runneth forward and back—*
For the strength of the Pack is the Wolf,
*   and the strength of the Wolf is the*
*   Pack.*

                              —Rudyard Kipling

Last summer Helga and I bought a day-old pig whom
we reared on a bottle. When he was a week old we
turned him into the garden with our capybara, a
Brazilian rodent, which at that time was twice as big
as the pig. Capy resented the presence of the pig in her

territory and ran it mercilessly until finally we put it in the barn for the winter.

In the spring we brought the pig back to the garden, a half-grown boar now, at least twice as big as the capybara. In spite of the reversal in the order of the animals' size and power, the hierarchy that had been established the summer before persisted. The capybara ran the huge squealing pig all around the garden and we had to take it back to the barn.

Once a hierarchy is established it tends to be remarkably stable and lasting. It is the basic pattern of organization in the world of living creatures. It is the way in which the nervous system of an individual chicken is arranged and the way the pecking order in a flock of chickens is organized. Wolves have a hierarchy within their pack; there are hierarchies in the flocks of all grazing animals.

Man organizes his societies in the same way animals do. His industries and his armies are disposed in ranks and orders; so also are his churches, clubs, and homes. Even communal societies, like the kibbutzim of Israel, contain hierarchies of influence. The great "classless" societies of Russia and China are among the most hierarchical of all. Human beings may be born with equal potential, but this equality does not persist when they find their places in their society.

Lorenz has stated that the hierarchy developed as an organization to prevent intraspecies strife. There may be brief quarrels or even lengthy fights during the period in which a hierarchy is being established, but once firmly organized, it tends to set up guidelines for behavior and thus reduces acts of aggression. If a hierarchy is abolished, as when a revolution occurs, each individual suddenly begins to behave as if his status were as high as anyone's. Chaos and conflict result, until a new hierarchical organization evolves. Then acts of aggression, which at first were overt, become redirected and are replaced, as is the case in the societies of animals, by symbols of aggression. Order is restored.

It is possible that for the first time in recorded history man is beginning to employ a symbolism similar to the threats and growls that animals use in place of bites and scratches. Today man's teeth and claws are the atomic bomb, but never, since the first two times that the power of this weapon was demonstrated, has it been used to kill. The skirmishes of armies using conventional weapons are as relatively harmless, compared to atomic potentials, as are the snapping and snarling of a wolf trying to elicit from another a gesture of submission. If we can further ritualize conventional warfare into some sort of struggle in an international court, the battle for peace might be won. Man might then be able to convince himself that aggression is not innate, a thesis for which there is much evidence.

The view that aggression is like hunger, an innate drive that requires gratification, stems from observations of animals that have been reared to exhibit aggressiveness. It takes no account of the fact that in the wild there is a hierarchy that prevents intraspecies acts of aggression, that animals can be reared in such a way that they show little aggressiveness, even toward natural enemies, nor does it recognize that of all creatures man is the least governed by instinct and the most susceptible to the influence of early training.

Naturalist Sally Carrighar, after searching in vain for a report of warlike behavior among animals in their normal uncrowded states, has concluded that there is "no evidence of clan aggressiveness which can be surely identified as an evolutionary source of human wars." She thinks that organized aggression is a social rather than a genetic phenomenon, and that it depends on education and training rather than on innate aggressiveness in the mind of man.

Anthropologist Margaret Mead explains the existence of war in the human race as the result of man's unique ability to symbolize. Through the use of such symbols as language, man is able to persuade himself that his own tribal or national groups belong to his particular species, but that others, who have different languages, customs, or religions, are subhuman and hence deserve to be dealt with as if they were predators of a different species.

Since language, customs, and religions are not innate, but are acquired by each individual through contacts with his society, it is likely that there are no genes for war, merely genes for developing the type of culture that leads to war.

If one considers aggressiveness to be not an instinctive and unalterable part of human nature, but as a pattern of behavior that an individual learns from his society, the conclusion is that it could be either induced or suppressed, depending on the way in which a child is reared. Loving, which is the counterpart of aggressiveness, can be profoundly affected by early environment. This suggests that loving behavior is not innate but is a potential that can be developed to its full only through experience. When the orphan children whom Bowlby described were raised without love, they did not grow up to miss it or to feel that they must express their pent-up love; they simply were unaware of it. Their potential for love had been suppressed by their early deprivation. The potential for aggression might similarly be suppressed if the child were surrounded with love and educated to cooperate instead of to compete. Equally important to him would be learning early in life how to replace acts of aggression with acts symbolic of aggressions, which were understood by the members of the hierarchy.

Although aggression is a strong force in establishing the hierarchy of society, the force of love or attraction is more powerful. It is this force which brings together molecules into cells, cells into animals, animals into societies, and societies into interdependence upon each other. From a biological standpoint, it seems that the dominant response of living things is not aggression, but attraction. I once saw an example of this in the Caribbean, where a school of jack fish had been netted and were circling slowly, unperturbed. When I lifted one out of the net and liberated it, the fish darted back, struggling to force its way through the meshes to join the others. When I picked it up and put it with the captured school again, it blended into the others, apparently content.

Attraction and aggression are at opposite ends of a spectrum of behavior. They may be continually modified, augmented, or suppressed by appropriate types of early training. If a child is taught consistently in school that he must be an individualistic and aggressive leader, it is difficult to see how he can be content when he has to take his place in the ladder of his society's hierarchy.

It would seem that the educational system today is designed to discourage the kind of cooperation necessary for the development of a highly organized society. From the student's first years in school, until he leaves college, often as a mature man, his success is never measured by his ability to cooperate, but by his competitive prowess. John Dewey said that so thoroughly was this the prevailing atmosphere that for one child to help another in his task became a school crime. Perhaps the emphasis upon never assisting one's fellow may be a poor way to prepare a child for his role in the future's society.

Nature has found two different ways of establishing a hierarchy of cells in a multicellular organism. In most creatures, the embryo originates as a single cell. In each succeeding generation of cells the descendants of the original ones specialize, losing some functions and gaining others, until none of the cells can survive alone and all must cooperate for the benefit of the whole creature. This is the usual and the most efficient way of developing the hierarchy of specialized cells that we call an animal.

The other, which is an apparently much less efficient path to specialization, is exemplified by the slime mold. This organism resembles a slug, but is made by the coming together of a large number of amoebas, which reproduce merely by splitting in two. All of them are independent and identical while they are swimming free, but if the pond in which they exist goes dry, the amoebas cluster together and take form. The resultant creature, now less susceptible to drying up than were the individuals of which it is made, can crawl along the ground in search of water. If it does not find it, there is further specialization of the originally identical-appearing amoebas. Some of them grow up in the form of stalks which then given rise to spores that are able to withstand a drought. When it rains and the pond fills, the spores become amoebas again and repopulate the water.

A century ago, when sons grew up to till their father's fields or follow his trade, the development of the social hierarchy evolved in a way that is similar to nature's usual and successful way of producing higher animals. Specialization started early in the period of the child's development. Each person was trained, as he was brought up, to fill a particular place in society. Today our schools are turning out children analogous rather to the amoebas of the slime mold, identical, unspecialized, competitive, and free-moving. They are graduated from schools that are almost exactly alike, at ages so advanced that it is difficult for them to specialize effectively in a trade or to understand the feel of tools that a skillful artisan should have. It is not easy for these competitively trained scholars to cooperate with one another or even to realize that the welfare of their society depends as much on their tolerance, willingness, and enthusiasm as on their individual technical abilities.

Perhaps the organization of our society has become so complex and the people in it so specialized and interdependent that a premium should be set on ability to cooperate instead of on competition within one's own group. Anthropologist Leach decries the competitiveness in England's educational system, saying, "Only a tiny minority thinks of education as a means by which individuals are given human interests and values so that they can fit together into the total jigsaw of society: for most of us education is an instrument of war, a weapon by which the individual beats down his competitors and defends himself against adversity." This weapon is unnecessary, for as a society matures and its individual members become more and more specialized and interdependent, there should be less and less need for competition within the society.

The term "society" once was used only in relationship to human beings. Then naturalists began to refer to "societies" of insects, and more recently, microbiologists speak of "societies" of cells. The arrangements of particles within cells are called "communities," implying that among them also is a social organization. André Lwoff, in his Nobel Laureate lecture, defined an organism as a "molecular society." He said also that "biological order is a kind of social order." It is thus becoming more and more difficult to draw a line between the animate and the inanimate, and to determine whether the term "society" can apply to organization among molecules as it does among insects, animals, and man.

Wolves have one of the most highly organized societies among the higher animals. There is almost no fighting within the pack and little between packs. Leadership is recognized and a well-defined hierarchy exists. The wolves cooperate in effecting their kill and they share the spoils. It seems likely that the organization of their society evolved slowly through the eons, being transmitted from generation to generation, just as accumulated knowledge is passed along by human beings. In primate societies this is also true. It was found that when young monkeys were separated from their societies and sent off to form a new one, chaos ensued. Although the environment of the island on which the new monkey colony was established was well suited for the animals to live in contentedly, their hierarchy had been disrupted and they quarreled and fought continuously.

In the lower animals, patterns of social behavior are indestructible as long as any breeding members of the society survive. Young insects, separated from their society, will grow up with full potential to organize a typical insect society. Their social traits are innate, being carried in their genes. On the other hand, the social behavior of the higher animals, including man, does not reside in the individuals themselves, but has evolved through the centuries among the individuals who compose the society. Thus an individual's behavior is less dependent on his "human nature" than on the nature of his society. In this connection, Nobel Laureate Paul Medawar has observed that mice do not lose their "mouselike" ways if at birth each generation is separated from all other mice, but that "the entire structure of human society as we know it, would be destroyed in a single generation if anything of the kind were to be done with man."

As a society develops, it continually molds the behavior of the individuals who compose it into more and more specialized channels. From the standpoint of evolution, it is perhaps no accident that in human society the trend in the last century has been toward increasing socialism. It may be that man is on his way toward developing a society like the ants', in which each individual is so dependent on the special services of others that no one can live for long alone. In the case of the ants, naturalists have questioned whether they are truly a colony of individuals or are a single superorganism, with the various parts dispersed and mobile, instead of being contained in one body. If the trend throughout the world continues toward a single type of complex industrial society, all peoples may become as dependent on their societies as the colonial insects are. As individuality diminishes, it is likely that a superorganism of human society will emerge. Before this occurs there are many barriers that will have to be broken down, among them the barrier of race.

Although the ability of people of all races to adapt to their particular environments seems to be similar, their customs are not, and neither, therefore, is the training their children receive. It is impossible to evaluate the innate aptitudes of different races, because the abilities of people depend as much on how they were reared as on their genetic constitution. Since there is so much variation in size, color, and facial characteristics, it is likely that there is variation also in such qualities as musical or mathematical ability. In this connection, Dwight Ingle, of the University of Chicago, says that genetically the average ability of members of different races cannot be expected to be equal in every field of endeavor, any more than one can expect the abilities of any two individuals of the same race to be equal. For this reason it would seem important to determine rather than to deny the differences. The time may come when all of mankind may benefit from some special quality that is most highly developed in one or another of the human races.

As human society becomes more and more dependent on the specialized functions of its various parts, it becomes more efficient and better able to support larger and larger populations. Sooner or later, however, the crowding will become intolerable. When that time comes, and if people are not willing to limit reproduction by their own individual efforts, it may be necessary for their societies to regulate it by law. It is likely, however, that automatic processes will prevail.

Among the arrangements that nature has made for perpetuation of various species are the mechanisms for automatic control of the growth of populations. Certain kinds of fish lay so many millions of eggs that, if they all hatched and the fishlets matured and spawned for a few generations, the sea would become solid with them. This does not happen, because the more a population increases, the more numerous its predators become and the less plentiful its food supply. By this Darwinian principle of survival, the populations of many species of lower animals are controlled.

Some of the higher animals, like lions, wolves, and men, have no predators to control their populations and they have plenty to eat. In their case, population appears to be controlled by their ability to recognize one another and take appropriate action. Even amoebas are able to recognize one another and when their population increases beyond a certain point, they stop reproducing. In some of the higher animals also, this type of mechanism seems to control the growth of populations.

Nearly half a century ago a group of wolves were marooned on Isle Royal in Lake Superior. Although

there was an adequate supply of food and no molesta-
tion from man or animal, their number and that of
the moose on which they fed remained relatively constant, under the observations of naturalists, for more
than twenty years. The control of the populations of
higher animals seems to depend on the development of
forms of social behavior which limit reproduction and
avoid overexploitation of food resources. Wild animals
in natural environments rarely die of starvation. Every
songbird defends its territory against others of its
kind. This keeps the population level low enough to
insure a food supply for all. Guppies, kept in a small
tank, will maintain their number at a certain point by
eating the young ones; if their population is reduced,
the cannibalism ceases. Lions, which have no natural
enemies, do not overpopulate their ranges; to do so
would exhaust their food supply. The great horned
owls usually nest with one pair to a territory, and they
never become abundant. Ethologists believe that predators and their prey live in a sort of subtle symbiosis,
which is advantageous to the evolutionary development of both.

In mankind the situation is more complex. Except
in a few primitive places, there are no natural enemies
to control his numbers. Science has gone far in curbing
infectious diseases. There is no innate mechanism, such
as many of the predators have, that limits the rate of
reproduction when populations get too dense. The
fetus of a fox, for example, will be absorbed in periods
of stress, but it seems that the control of the population

of human beings will have to be by their own planned action. In some primitive areas, such arrangements already exist as a result of sexual taboos and infanticide.

Certain countries have found ways to limit the growth of their populations, the Irish by late marriage or celibacy, the Japanese and Swedes by contraception and abortion. In most of the industrialized nations, the birthrates have fallen to such an extent that the population is barely replacing itself. The Chinese too are experimenting with birth control and providing incentives for limiting the size of families.

In the countries which control the growth of their populations, the people have been motivated by the opportunities afforded by their expanding industrial societies. They act not from fear of privation but from an interest in having their children obtain a good education and a stable position in the social scale.

Although many sociologists deny that population pressure is a common cause of war, there is little doubt that crowding promotes the violence that takes place in urban slums. This may be because man is a territorial animal and behaves according to a series of distances which have been defined by Hediger. The "flight distance" is the distance to which an animal will allow a potential enemy to approach before fleeing, or if cornered, before being forced to attack. This distance seems to be precise for each interspecies encounter. In a large animal such as a deer it will be hundreds of yards, and in a tiny reptile, only a few feet.

Whereas "flight distance" applies to interspecies

spacing, "personal distance" is the regular spacing which occurs between individuals of the same species. Walruses, pigs, and parakeets, for example, favor close physical contact. Other species, such as dogs, rats, hawks, apes, and man, are noncontact species and avoid touching. A human being's "personal distance" may be measured by the amount of crowding he will tolerate from members of his own kind. If crowded beyond these limits, he may be impelled either to retreat or attack. Since in the crowded slums there is no empty space for retreat, the alternative is apt to be aggressive behavior.

Aggression need not take the form of violence. The social signals like snarling or hissing which animals use to warn one another are learned in infancy and youth, without resorting to the aggressive act that they imply. If mankind were able to communicate in a similar clear way that would be understood by all, his societies might be as free of conflict and violence as is that of animals in their natural environment. Man, however, communicates through language, and words do not mean the same things to all people. The difficulty is that people of various races have different ways of expressing delight, anger, or fear. If the symbols are misunderstood, tragedies may occur, similar to those which take place when creatures of different species become engaged in a fight.

If a fight occurs between two members of the same species, each understands the other's symbols. When wild turkeys are battling, and one of them wishes to give up, he uses a symbol of submission, which is to lie on the ground with outstretched neck. The victorious turkey may strut about his fallen foe and peck at his body, but he will not harm the vulnerable neck. This understanding of the symbol of subjugation is innate. However, if a turkey and a peacock are fighting in a barnyard, death may result, for the signal of the extended neck will not be heeded by the peacock.

It is unlikely that mere translation of the existing national languages will accomplish worldwide understanding among mankind. Subtle connotations and meanings are too often lost. Arthur Larson, director of the World Rule of Law Center at Duke University, thinks it might be done through an international language of law which would be used by world courts. This might not be successful, for human beings are so diverse that difficulties often arise even when a person tries to do unto another as he would like to be done by. In nature, and in contacts between different human cultures, the golden rule simply doesn't work. To feed a creature that is different from yourself a diet whose only recommendation is that you like it is to court disaster. The same principle applies to the customs of man, for what is pleasing to people of one society may be abhorrent to those of another. Thus, no matter how dedicated an advanced society is to the principles of democracy, it cannot successfully impose these principles in an underdeveloped country with an illiterate population.

Each type of life and each stage of development of

human society makes its own special demands on nature. Many of these demands are for what seems to be harsh treatment. Thus the seeds of the wild tomatoes of the Galapagos Islands will not germinate unless they have passed through the intestines of the Galapagos tortoises or have been partially digested by soaking them in Clorox. Seeds of northern wildflowers may have to be frozen before they will germinate. If not so treated, they are easily killed by the type of kindness that we bestow on the common seeds of the garden. By the same token, there may be times in the development of a human society in which it will thrive best under what members of a more advanced society might consider a harsh dictatorship.

In addition to the misunderstandings that occur accidentally or as a result of the differences in the stages of development of different cultures, there is the added problem of the planned and calculated aggression we call war. This is fostered by the study of history and literature that glorify the heroes of wars. From childhood on, man's memories are replete with lurid details of violence. It seems that he has made a conscious effort in his literature, art, and entertainment to perpetuate war between individuals and groups.

Lecky states that one of the factors that contributed to the downfall of Rome was the emphasis placed on the gladiatorial games and on cruelty. Nero, he said, was the most beloved of all the Roman emperors because of his munificence in providing spectacles of bloodshed, death, and torture in the Colosseum for the amusement of the public of all classes. Animals and men alike were employed in every variety of atrocity and barbarity. On one occasion four hundred tigers fought with bulls and elephants; again four hundred bears and three hundred lions were slaughtered; rhinoceroses, bulls, stags, hippopotami, even serpents and crocodiles were captured and put into the arena. Human suffering was presented in every form; ten thousand gladiators fought during the games of Trajan, and eight hundred pair of them clashed at the triumph of Aurelian. The sport became so popular that in spite of special laws that forbade it, certain patricians became gladiators. Children were a part of the throngs since infancy, and imitated the gladiators in their play.

The historians who wrote of this bloodshed during these times never seemed to be aware that they were recording a barbarity. Perhaps they felt as Spaniards do today about bullfights, which they have been accustomed to attend since small children. It seems that often the greatest humanitarians have been unable to view objectively their own societies. Religious persecution, the slaughter of savages, and the practice of making slaves of men were accepted almost without question in their day, just as modern man accepts the barbarities continually shown on the television screen.

A recent experiment shows how habits of social conformity and submission to authority can cause normal people to perform, on command, acts of the greatest cruelty. Dr. S. Milgram, a psychologist, recruited forty volunteers from a wide range of occupations, who were told that the purpose of the experiment was to study the effects of punishment on learning. One of Dr. Milgram's associates, masquerading as a volunteer, was strapped into an electric chair, above which was a complex instrument panel with switches labeled from "slight shock" to "danger, severe shock." The volunteer believed he was giving increasingly greater punishment to the victim, who pretended to be suffering more and more as the switches labeled with higher voltages were pulled. Finally the subject lapsed into silence, inert. At this point, the volunteers were encouraged to continue to give the shocks, and although they showed extreme agitation while doing it, twenty-six of the forty gave what they thought were shocks up to 450 volts to the seemingly suffering subject. While some of the participants protested, they continued to obey instructions to the end, for the experiment was being done under the auspices of a respected university. They were not cruel, yet their compliance to the orders suggests that when a practice is accepted by a society, the individual rarely objects.

My father, during the First World War, wrote that the earliest predisposing cause of the conflict was the establishment of an action pattern of war in the child, and that this event was a microscopic declaration of war. Multiples of like action patterns made inevitable the final declaration of war between the nations. "The young of all animals are plastic," he said. "The child of man is most plastic. If a child remains in a Christian portion of the web of life, Christian action patterns are formed; if in a pagan web, he becomes pagan; if in a peaceful web, peaceful action patterns result; if in a warlike web, warlike patterns are inevitable. The brain patterns that dominate at the close of the adolescent and at the beginning of the adult period fix and determine until death the life reactions of the individual . . . the molten metal adapts itself the mold—the mold remains unchanged. The only way by which the action patterns of a people can be altered is by changing the mold—altering the environment. Thus slowly science and invention and human experience modify the mold which stamps generations to come."

It is possible that both war and religion have been of survival value to human societies. They have spurred men on to the discovery of how to make not only better steel, but also bigger pyramids and cathedrals. Often the knowledge gained in these ways gave such clear superiority to the culture that developed it that other cultures were forced to adopt the ways of the dominant one. In short, until the twentieth century the chief spurs to technical advances may have been war and religion.

In the last fifty years industry and the state have begun to support research. As a result, science is no longer dependent on the incentives provided by war or religion, but has become an end in itself. Man has begun to recognize that the success of his society and the prolongation of his way of life depend more on skills derived from research than on strength of arms or prayer. The question now arises whether development of the concept of science has not rendered obsolete the spurs of war and religion that for so long have goaded men to technical achievements. Today, for example, the effort expended on exploring outer space is giving technological leadership to the countries that are in the race for the moon. In view of these stimuli, is it necessary to continue to tell young children that they must resort to war, if necessary, to defend their nationalistic, cultural, or religious beliefs? Through the centuries it has been dogmatic beliefs, instilled into children in their formative years, that have caused the intolerances that so often have led to war.

Another cause of war is the rigidity of the hierarchy of human society. Usually the leaders of a nation's hierarchy are beyond the age of fifty. As we have observed before, it is difficult for men of this age to be receptive to new ideas or tolerant of those which differ from their own.

In ancient times, when innovations were few and problems remained much the same from generation to generation, it was the elders who had the most experience and had the greatest wisdom. Now with changes occurring so rapidly, a vast knowledge of the past may not be as valuable as an understanding of the present. It is interesting to speculate as to what might have happened at the Yalta Conference if Roosevelt had not been in his final illness, Churchill, as Lord Moran reports, had not been already afflicted with many transient symptoms of senility, and if Stalin had not been the victim of the paranoia that Svetlana describes.

Leaders, it seems, are often those who in their youth had vision and imagination enough to outstrip their competitors. The rest of their lives they spend not in advancing further but in defending their positions while the rest of the world catches up. It is therefore strange that, in this era of change, there is no mandatory retirement age for politicians.

Older men, regardless of their abilities, tend to become so set in their ways that they are not able to recognize changes or adapt to them. They continue to view things in much the same way as they did when they first made up their minds about them. It is also to the interest of those in the hierarchy who are close to the leaders to support them in their positions, for if the leaders fall, the followers fall with them. In connection with this rigidity of the hierarchy, Walter Lippmann recently noted ". . . since President Kennedy's death our foreign policy has been conducted by men whose minds were formed and whose convictions hardened about twenty-five years ago."

Perhaps the greatest barrier to human beings learning to understand others who come from a different society is their ability to think in terms of right and wrong. The members of each society know the way they do something and are apt to think any other way of doing it is not only wrong, but a threat to what they consider to be the right way. They do not realize that nature has found many different ways of accomplishing her purposes. Thus porpoises, which are mammals, outswim all fish. Bats, also mammals, outfly many birds. Societies of animals, and of peoples too, may reach their aims in diverse ways. Galbraith, in his essays on economics, has shown the similarity between the achievements of government-planned, highly socialized industries and of those which evolved in capitalistic countries through free enterprise. Between these different cultures, it is not the end results that are in dispute, but the ways of reaching them. For example, it is interesting to speculate on what might have happened in the United States if instead of breaking up trusts, the Government had allowed monopolies to develop and then, as in the case of the telephone companies, had regulated prices and set ceilings on profits. It is possible that the organization of our industries would by now be quite similar to that which prevails in the most advanced of the Communist countries.

Communism, in the areas in which it has been accepted, is not only a political system, but a way of life, a kind of religion. When a child of one society is reared to think that a certain religious belief is the only true one, it may be difficult for him to accept or even to comprehend those who have been reared with different concepts. This is the kind of misunderstanding which motivated the Crusades. In those senseless wars, which lasted for more than a hundred years, even children marched to save the Holy Land. Generation after generation were successfully indoctrinated with the notion of crusading.

Man has been reared to believe that wars and violence are a part of human heritage. Perhaps all that need be done to abolish them would be to bring up one generation throughout the world without the images of violence. It is within the power of each nation to rear a generation of children without belief that their country is always right or that their religion is the true one. Man makes the mistake, it seems, of trying to prevent warfare and destruction by appealing to adults, rather than by simply rearing his children to the images of peace. The situation brings to mind a school of blackfish I once saw off the coast of Yucatan.

Helga and I were skindiving close to shore with a native, when he pointed to a dark area fifty yards in diameter looming ahead like a reef in the bright blue water. We swam out to it, in water ten feet deep, and came to a solid wall of dark-scaled, basslike fish, packed closely from the bottom to the surface, circling slowly in a clockwise direction. As I swam into the midst of them, they parted. When I had passed, they closed ranks and continued again in their circle. The native said that the fish had come there three years before and never left the spot, always swimming in the same pattern. Because none of the fishermen had ever seen anything like it, they considered it a sort of miracle and by common consent left the fish undisturbed.

I have since asked ichthyologists why the fish kept circling there, but never obtained a firm answer. My theory is that the fish were swimming in a school across the Yucatan channel when they reached land. The leaders turned back and came within sight of the fish at the end of the column and began to follow them. A circuit movement, like that of auricular fibrillation in the muscle of the heart, was started. Once begun, it could not stop. Friends visiting the area recently report that the fish are still there, still circling, confidently following their leaders. The famous French naturalist Jean Henri Fabre observed a similar phenomenon in a group of processionary caterpillars, creatures who when they march follow one another blindly. Fabre enticed the caterpillars onto the rim of a flowerpot and succeeded in getting the first one of the line to follow the last in line, closing the circle. For a week the caterpillars followed one another around the pot, disregarding nearby food, until finally they dropped of starvation and exhaustion.

Something like the blackfish's accident may be what has happened to mankind in his generation-to-generation circuit of war and destruction. Perhaps what is needed is a new start—not a new religion or a new belief, but the application of what is already known about education and the rearing of children. We have learned that the basic reactions of people to their environments are instilled in them in the first decade of their lives. It should not be difficult to instill, in a new generation, a feeling of their responsibilities to their environments and to their fellowmen.

From the time that life on earth first appeared, its development was directed by the slow force of evolution. Then came the exponential growth of man's population and of his technology. The changes that man now makes, year by year, in the ecology of his environment, dwarf those effected by millennia of organic evolution. These changes are being made too rapidly for organic evolution to compensate for errors.

The theme of this book is that there is a critical period, in the development of each organism, at which time the creature is particularly vulnerable to an abnormality in its environment and especially fitted to make an adaptive change. As a result of the development of the new type of man-made evolution, the superorganism of the world seems to be in one of these critical periods. Never has there been a time more appropriate for an adaptive change than is this time for educating the children of the world about the seriousness of the menace that confronts them. Never has it been more essential that men of all technologically advanced nations forbear from teaching their children their particular nationalistic, racial, or religious dogmas. The time has come to cooperate in rearing a generation unified in a common knowledge of science and in dedication to peace. To make this utopian plan a reality it will be necessary to have the urgency of the threat and the critical state of the world's ecology understood by the political and religious leaders of the world. They will have to be persuaded to support an educational program of a type that has never before existed. Perhaps this will be possible, for the present crisis is like that of a country being laid waste by tribal warfare, but which, when attacked from without, stops its internal feuding and unites to resist the common enemy.

The enemy of the human race, if not of all higher forms of life, is technology misused to destroy the natural environment of the earth. The depredations of this vigorous hybrid, sprung from the union of science and fossil fuels, can be seen in wasted lands, crowded cities, and polluted air, streams, and seas. Since these changes will soon be apparent to all men everywhere, it may not be utopian to believe that, in the face of a common danger, ancient prejudices will be dropped, and men of all countries will work together for their mutual salvation. If they could be persuaded to do so, they could build a plastic and adaptable hierarchy to administrate an educational system based on science. Such a program, taught in a common second language in nursery schools, preschools, and grade schools throughout the world could rear a generation trained from infancy in the language of science, cooperation, and peace.

CHAPTER TEN

Return to Pan

*But ask now the beasts, and they shall
teach thee; and the fowls of the air; and
they shall tell thee: or speak to the earth,
and it shall teach thee: and the fishes of
the sea shall declare unto thee.*
— Job 12: 7–10

Our country house is built into a wooded hillside and
is composed of a single large room on the ground floor,
and an open balcony above the back half. Helga's desk
is at the upper-story rail where she overlooks my work-
table, as well as the garden beyond the windows. Our
imprinted crow and vultures perch nearby on a log or
tree limb where they can watch us. The two deer spend
much of their time peering in, and as the peacocks and
geese and varied fowl in the yard go about, they stop to
look in on us. The white swan even leaves his pool to
waddle majestically up the slope to see what is going on
inside. None of the creatures is to be found in the

far corners of the garden; they seem to take as great an interest in our affairs as we do in theirs.

No one knows what goes on in the minds of these animals, but they seem to live in a state of serenity and acceptance and to feel that we are a part of their lives. Between them and us is a strong bond, not only because of our affection for them and our pleasure in their beauty, but also due to the link they give us to nature. They tie us to our childhoods and, as well, to the far past of mankind recorded in our racial memory.

Centuries ago, in the period of the Classical Greek civilization, science was in its infancy, but the reverence that human beings felt for the natural world about them was perhaps at its height. The god Pan was said to live then. His name meant *all*, and he was the representative of nature. He was mischievous, lusty, and at peace with the animals of the woods and fields. The imaginative Greeks invested even the inanimate world with gods—Neptune ruled the sea, Zeus the sky. The cosmos was united in the persons of the deities. All natural phenomena were ascribed to their agency.

With the aid of science, man has now produced for himself powers which are so great as to rival those originally ascribed to the gods, including, to a limited degree, the power to prolong life, to restore life to the newly dead, to harness the energy of both molecule and atom, and to create the substance of life itself. Along with these powers there now is beginning to develop, as in the days of Pan, a concept of a cosmos which is a unity and has no beginning and no end. There is no boundary between zero and infinity, no discontinuity between what always has been and what will be forevermore. There is no line of division between the inanimate elements of which the world is composed and the complex organizations of chemicals that result in what is called life. Finally we are beginning to realize that there is no sharp distinction between the ways of animals and of man, or between human morality and the validity of natural laws.

The pagan's creed of Pan encompassed a host of symbolic gods that unified man's concept of the universe into a single complex belief. This creed, in reverse, is becoming popular with some scientists today, who believe that it is as unifying to have no gods for anything as to have gods for everything. The danger is to believe that the divine spark resides in Christians but not in Muhammadans, in man but not in animals—to have gods for churches but none for the waters, the forests, and the fields.

In the physical world from which life evolved, there are repetitive patterns of form and activity. Electrons whirl about their nucleus, the moon circles the earth, and the earth revolves around the sun. This principle may go on in orbital patterns, one nebula circling another, into infinity. In the world of the living, there are repetitive patterns also. The behavior of a one-celled amoeba has analogies in the behavior of higher animals as well as in that of human beings. Similarities may be observed between the factors influencing the development of individual men and those affecting the organization of human societies.

The arrangement of a vast city, seen from a plane at night with its processions of lighted cars streaming through the urban arteries, is strikingly like the appearance of a living cell or a living creature under a microscope. Millions of people have come together to form the city, just as millions of cells have done for the animal. Each living thing, whether it be an individual cell, a group of cells that are united to make up a body, or a group of creatures organized in a society, evolved from a simple beginning. The course of its evolution, whether into cell or city, depends on the time at which events occur. Nothing is ever the same from one moment to the next. In the words of Heraclitus, one of the first to grasp the importance of time in evolutionary change, "We never descend twice into the same stream."

Man has only begun to study the principles nature has used to accomplish her ends. It is not known how the navigational system of the sea turtle brings it back across the thousands of miles of trackless seas to lay eggs on the same beach on which it was hatched. Little is known about the marvels of "inner space," the reticulum of particles, each precisely organized in relationship to a myriad of others in each individual living cell. Man still knows nothing about what lies beyond the range of his telescopes or what energies, other than those already discovered, are helping to shape his life.

No one knows whether, in the days when Pan ruled over nature, mankind was more enchanted with his world than he is today. Perhaps he was, for the concept of a god is easier for many people to grasp than a scientific principle. Yet now, when there is ready access to all the aids and skills which can be employed for teaching children, it ought to be possible to transmit to them not only an outline of all the basic information about what is known of the universe, but at the same time a sense of wonder about those mysteries not as yet explored.

When I was ten years old, radio was just coming in. Crystal sets were not yet for sale in stores but you could make them yourself. I spent long hours exploring the shiny bits of galena with the whisker of bronze wire, searching for the sensitive spot which would bring me music from the air. It was a mystic experience, and I had a sense of disbelief and wonder about this development of radio that had taken place so suddenly in the short span of my life. I wonder if children today are still able to be stirred by contemporary developments in science and technology or if they have become so used to innovation that it no longer seems miraculous to them.

Today there would seem to be greater physical security than there has ever been before. Human beings no longer live in dread of starvation or plague. However, the symbols of insecurity are everywhere. Mankind imbues his children with a dread of solitude, of failure, of the loss of status or wealth, or the enigma of his life coming to an end. The imagination of modern man has presented him with images far more terrifying than those of certain of the gods with which the pagans peopled their world. Yet if we chose to do so we could rear our children to have no dread either of life or of death. The means are now at our disposal. If we started in earliest childhood we could teach a generation of children to enjoy natural pleasures, to have realistic values, and to live in their world content.

It has been said that in the predawn of human history, man became committed to the use of the mechanism of words, with their static meaning, instead of a form which might have allowed him to reproduce more faithfully the fluent characters of things as they are. The statement is valid, for the universe is not static, as our descriptions of it imply, it is not composed of bits and parts, it is dynamic. It flows through space and time. Each bit of the universe is connected by its radiation or by its gravitational force to each other bit. In the ecology of the living world each creature is dependent on each other one and on the entire web of life. Every bit of the universe is interconnected, but in order to learn about it we dissect it and study it apart from the reality of its interrelations. When we describe what we have learned about nature in the symbolism of our language, we strive to establish qualitative differences that make each part distinct from the others and therefore a recognizable entity, easy for the teacher to describe and the student to remember. In this way the concept of the fluidity and continuity of the universe is disrupted and there emerges an image that has been partitioned into a myriad of artificial fragments. It is therefore small wonder that students do not find in science, as it is taught, a unifying and satisfying basis for understanding themselves and their universe. It is not surprising that children reared in this way fail to find continuity even within their own human kind, nor that they make war against those they have been taught to view as different and discontinuous from themselves.

It may be that not only most of the attainments of mankind, but also most of his sufferings, have risen as the result of his ability to use the symbolism of words. The chronic discontent which springs from this symbolism is reminiscent of Montaigne's account of King Pyrrhus who told his queen, Cyneas, that he wanted to conquer Italy, then Gaul and Spain and Africa. "Then when I have the whole World to my Subjection, I will rest content, and live at my own Ease," he said. Cyneas replied, "For God's Sake, Sir, Tell me what hinders that you may not if you please be now in that condition? Why do you not now, at this instant, settle yourself in the state you say you aim at, and spare yourself the Labor and Hazard you must encounter."

Evolution has appointed the race to what Julian Huxley called the "cosmic office" of being in charge of evolution itself. It is therefore essential that there be developed a system which will limit man's depredation not only of his own kind, but of the plant and animal populations with which he lives. The world is a superorganism of which man is only a part. It is made up of a few score of elementary chemicals in various combinations, and of a myriad separate units of life. Each species is like an organ of the superorganism. Each has a specific function; each is important to the economy of the whole. If within the superorganism there is unlimited growth of one species at the expense of the others, it is not only the welfare of the super-organism that is at stake, but also that of the species that consumes it. It is the way of tumors, having lost their response to the mechanisms which control their growth, to destroy first their hosts, then themselves.

Since Darwin, science has been in its ascendancy, but in its teachings there has been little conscious attempt to cultivate beauty or to instruct in reverence or love. No dominant humanistic philosophy has yet grown out of science. Now that the world of mankind is becoming so crowded, the billions spent yearly upon the technology of war and space travel might be channeled into the education of a single generation of children to a better understanding of themselves and the patterns of nature. Such an understanding will not be possible until we instill in children, before the age of seven, an understanding of themselves, their kind, their ecology, and their universe.

Peace is nature's way. Outside the glass windows of the Unicorn's Lair are the fallow deer, the vultures, the capybara, the crow, the swan, and a variety of other birds and beasts who are often thought not to live so harmoniously together. Because all of them were brought into the garden as babies and were reared to peace, they have no animosities toward each other. They accept trouble with equanimity and pleasure without remorse.

BIBLIOGRAPHY

CHAPTER ONE

Anfinsen, C. B. *The Molecular Basis of Evolution.* New York, John Wiley and Sons, 1966.

Bowlby, J. *Maternal Care and Mental Health.* World Health Organization. Monograph Ser. 2, 1952.

Frisch, K. von. *Man and the Living World.* New York, Harcourt, Brace & World, 1962.

Griffin, E. I. "Making Friends With a Killer Whale." *National Geographic,* March 1966, p. 418.

Harlow, H. F., and Harlow, M. K. "Social Deprivation in Monkeys." *Scientific American* 207 : 136–146, November 1962.

Loeb, L. *The Biological Basis of Individuality.* Springfield, Illinois, Charles C. Thomas, 1945.

Lorenz, K. *King Solomon's Ring.* New York, Thomas Crowell Company, 1952.

Market, C. L. "Biochemical Events during Differentiation. General Survey." *The Journal of Experimental Zoology* 157 : 81–84, October 1964.

Morris, D. "The Naked Ape." *Life,* December 22, 1967.

Reynolds, V. *The Apes: The Gorilla, Chimpanzee, Orangutan, and Gibbon—Their History and Their World.* New York, Dutton, 1967. (Reviewed by Barnett, S. A., *Book World,* December 31, 1967.)

Steward, S. C. "The Control of Growth in Plant Cells." *Scientific American* 209 : 104, October 1963.

Thorpe, W. H. *Biology and the Nature of Man.* London, Oxford University Press, 1962.

Thorpe, W. H. *Learning and Instinct in Animals.* Cambridge, Mass., Harvard University Press, 1963.

Thorpe, W. H. Quoted by Carrighar, S. in "War Is Not In Our Genes." *The New York Times Magazine,* September 10, 1967, p. 74.

Weiss, P. "The Problem of Cellular Differentiation." *Proceedings of the National Cancer Conference,* 1959, p. 50.

CHAPTER TWO

Agranoff, B. W., and Klinger, P. D. "Puromycin Effect on Memory Fixation in the Goldfish." *Science* 146 : 952–953, November 13, 1964.

Babich, F. R., Jacobson, A. L., Bubash, S., and Jacobson, A. "Transfer of a Response to Naive Rats by Injection of Ribonucleic Acid Extracted from Trained Rats." *Science* 149 : 656–657, August 6, 1965.

Cameron, D. E., and Solyom, L. "Effects of Ribonucleic Acid on Memory." *Geriatrics* 16 : 74, 1961.

Fiske, D. W., and Maddi, S. R., eds. *Functions of Varied Experience.* Homewood, Illinois, Dorsey Press, 1961.

Gelber, B. "Investigations of the Behavior of *Paramecium aurelia:* I. Modification of Behavior after Training with Reinforcement." *The Journal of Comparative and Physiological Psychology* 45 : 58–65, 1952.

Gelber, B. "Retention in Paramecium Aurelia." *The Journal of Comparative and Physiological Psychology* 51 : 110–115, 1958.

Grohmann, J. "Modifikation oder Funktionsreifung?" *Zeitschrift für Tierpsychologie* 2 : 132–144, 1939.

Jacobson, A. L. "Learning in Flatworms and Annelids." *Psychology Bulletin* 60 : 74–94, January 1963.

Koestler, A. *The Ghost in the Machine.* New York, Macmillan Company, 1967.

Lorenz, K. *Evolution and Modification of Behavior.* Chicago, University of Chicago Press, 1965.

McConnell, J. V. "The Modern Search for the Engrain," *Naturwissenschaft und Medicin* Jahrgang 2, 1965. Heft 9 seite 14, Heransgeber. C. G. Boehringer & Soehne GmbH, Mannheim.

McConnell, J. V. Quoted by Appel, F.C. in "Experts Disagree on a Worm's I.Q." *The New York Times,* February 14, 1965, p. 76.

Thorpe, W. H. *Learning and Instinct in Animals.* Cambridge, Mass., Harvard University Press, 1963.

Tinbergen, N. *The Study of Instinct.* Oxford, England, Clarendon Press, 1951.

Watanabe, T. "Infectious Drug Resistance." *Scientific American* 217 : 19–27, December 1967.

CHAPTER THREE

Gray, P. H. "Theory and Evidence of Imprinting in Human Infants." *Journal of Psychology* 46 : 155, 1958.

Hess, E. H. "Imprinting." *Science* 130 : 133–141, July 17, 1959.

Hess, E. H. "Imprinting in Birds." *Science* 146 : 1128–1139, November 27, 1964.

Leopold, W. F. *Speech Development of a Bilingual Child.* 4 Vols., Evanston, Illinois, Northwestern University Press, 1939–1949.

Penfield, W. "The Interpretive Cortex." *Science* 129 : 1719–1725, June 26, 1959.

Penfield, W. "Conditioning the Uncommitted Cortex for Language Learning." *Brain* 88 : 787–798, 1965.

Penfield, W., and Roberts, L. *Speech and Brain Mechanisms*. Princeton, Princeton University Press, 1959.

Spitz, R. A., and Cobliner, W. *The First Year of Life*. New York, International Universities Press, 1965.

Suzuki's Talent Education Institute. "Invasion from the Orient." *Time*, November 3, 1967, p. 46.

CHAPTER FOUR

Birch, H. G. "The Relation of Previous Experience to Insightful Problem-Solving." *Journal of Comparative Physiology and Psychology* 38 : 367–383, 1945.

Fisher, D. C. *A Montessori Mother*. New York, Holt, 1912.

Harlow, H. F., Harlow, M. K., and Meyer, D. R. "Learning Motivated by a Manipulation Drive." *Journal of Experimental Psychology* 40 : 228–234, 1950.

Hebb, D. O. "The Effects of Early Experience on Problem-Solving at Maturity." *American Psychologist* 2 : 306–307, 1947.

Hindley, C. "Ability and Social Class." *The Listener*, March 31, 1966, p. 464.

Hunt, J. McV. *Intelligence and Experience*. New York, Ronald Press, 1961.

Hunt, J. McV. Introduction to *The Montessori Method*, by Maria Montessori. New York, Schocken Books, 1964.

Lorenz, K. *On Aggression*. New York, Harcourt, Brace & World, 1966.

Montaigne's Essays, Vol. 1, seventh ed., London, 1759, p. 183.

Piaget, J. *Language and Thought of the Child*. New York, Meridian Books, 1955.

Pines, M., and Moore, O. K. *The Crucial Years of Learning: From Birth to Six.* New York, Harper & Row, 1967.

Rand, A. "Development and Enemy Recognition of Curved Bill Thrasher." *Bulletin of the American Museum of Natural History,* 78 : 213–242, 79 : 517–524, 1941.

Skeels, H. M., and Dye, H. B. "A Study of the Effects of Differential Stimulation on Mentally Retarded Children." *American Association on Mental Deficiency—Proceedings and Addresses of the 63rd Annual Session:* 114–136, 1939.

Skinner, B. F. "The Technology of Teaching." *Proceedings of The Royal Society,* Ser. B 162 : 427–443, July 27, 1965.

Terrace, H. S. "Errorless Transfer of a Discrimination Across Two Continua." *Journal of the Experimental Analysis of Behavior* 6 : 223–232, 1963.

Thompson, W. R., and Heron, W. "The Effects of Restricting Early Experience on the Problem-Solving Capacity of Dogs." *Canadian Journal of Psychology* 8 : 17–31, March 1954.

Time on Head Start, May 13, 1966, p. 27.

CHAPTER FIVE

Agranoff, B. W. "Molecules and Memories." *Perspectives in Biology and Medicine* 9 : 13–22. Chicago, University of Chicago Press, Autumn 1965.

Barth, L. G. "Developmental Physiology." *Annual Review of Physiology* 19 : 41–58, 1957.

Bruner, J. S. *The Process of Education.* Cambridge, Massachusetts, Harvard University Press, 1960.

Bruner, J. S. Quoted in "Preschool Boom: Its Pressures and Rewards." *Newsweek,* May 16, 1966, p. 109.

Dewey J., and Dewey, E. *Schools of Tomorrow.* New York, Dutton, 1915.

Goodman, P. *Compulsory Mis-education.* Horizon Press, 1964.

Goslin, D. A. "Standardized Ability Tests and Testing." *Science* 159 : 851–855, February 23, 1968.

Gray, J. G. "Salvation on the Campus: Why Existentialism Is Capturing the Students." *Harper's Magazine,* May 1965, pp. 53–59.

James, W. in *Treasury of Philosophy,* Runes, D. R., ed. New York, Philosophical Library, 1955.

Lorenz, K. *On Aggression.* New York, Harcourt, Brace & World, 1966.

Luria, A. R. *The Mind of a Mnemonist.* New York, Basic Books, 1968, pp. 11–12.

Markert, C. "Pathways of the Fountain of Youth." *Journal of Experimental Zoology* 157 : 81–84, October 1964.

Padilla, S. G. "Further Studies on the Delayed Feeding of Chicks." Thesis, University of Michigan Library. *Journal of Comparative Physiology and Psychology* 20 : 413–443, 1935.

Penfield, W. "Conditioning the Uncommitted Cortex for Language Learning." *Brain* 88 : 787–798, 1965.

Penfield, W., and Roberts, L. *Speech and Brain Mechanisms.* Princeton, Princeton University Press, 1959.

Pickering, G. "The Great Value of Ignorance." *Medical World News,* June 11, 1965, p. 74.

Snow, C. P. Prefatory note to *The Search.* New York, Charles Scribner's Sons, 1934; quoted in *Science* 130 : 419, August 21, 1959.

Spalding, D. "Instinct with Original Observations on Young Animals," 1872; reprinted in *British Journal of Animal Behaviour* 2 : 2–11, 1954.

Sperry, R. W. "The Growth of Nerve Circuits." *Scientific American* 201 : 68–75, November 1959.

Spitz, R. A. *No and Yes: On the Genesis of Human Communication.* New York, International Universities Press, 1957.

Thorpe, W. H. *Learning and Instinct in Animals.* Cambridge, Mass., Harvard University Press, 1963.

Underwood, B. J. "Forgetting." *Scientific American* 210 : 91–99, March 1964.

Weiss, P., editor. *Genetic Neurology. Problems of the Development, Growth, and Regeneration of the Nervous System and of Its Functions.* Chicago, University of Chicago Press, 1950.

CHAPTER SIX

Alsop, S. "A Conversation with Catfish." *The Saturday Evening Post,* February 24, 1968, p. 18.

Bowlby, J. *Maternal Care and Mental Health.* World Health Organization. Monograph Ser. 2, 1952.

Brain, R. Quoted by Penfield, W., and Roberts, L. *Speech and Brain Mechanisms.* Princeton, Princeton University Press, 1959.

Downes, D. "The Gang Myth." *The Listener,* April 14, 1966, p. 534.

Eysenck, H. J. "A Mystic Trade." *New Scientist,* March 24, 1966, p. 793.

First Book of Samuel, 16 : 23.

Gray, J. G., *op. cit.,* p. 53.

Harlow, H. F., Dodsworth, R. O., and Harlow, M. K. "Total Social Isolation in Monkeys." *Proceedings of the National Academy of Science* 54 : 90, July 1965.

Hess, E. H., et al. *The Pharmacology and Clinical Usefulness of Carisoprodol,* Miller, J. G., ed. Detroit, Wayne State University Press, 1959.

Leach, E. "Men and Learning." *The Listener,* December 14, 1967, p. 779.

Leach, P. "The Rigid Child." *The Listener,* March 24, 1966, p. 429.

Lorenz, K. *Man Meets Dog.* Baltimore, Penguin Books, 1965.

Lorenz, K. *On Aggression.* New York, Harcourt, Brace & World, 1966.

Montaigne's Essays, Vol. 1, seventh ed. London, 1759.

Redl, F. Quoted by Denenberg, V. H. "Early Experience and Emotional Development." *Scientific American* 208 : 138–146, June 1963.

Sachar, E. J. "Behavioral Science and Criminal Law." *Scientific American* 209 : 39–45, November 1963.

Spitz, R. A. "Hospitalism." *The Psychoanalytic Study of the Child* 2 : 113. New York, International Universities Press, 1946.

Williams, G. *Adaptation and Natural Selection: A Critique of Some Current Evolutionary Thought.* Princeton, Princeton University Press, 1966.

Wootton, B. "What Is Crime?" *The Listener,* April 28, 1966, p. 599.

CHAPTER SEVEN

Bingham, H. C. "Sex Development in Apes." *Comparative Psychology Monographs* 5 : 1–165, May 1928.

Cameron, R. *The Golden Haze.* Cleveland, The World Publishing Company, 1964.

Craig, W. "The Voices of Pigeons Regarded as a Means of Social Control." *American Journal of Sociology* 14 : 86, 1908.

Guze, H. "Research on Sex." *Science* 151 : 675–677, February 11, 1966.

Harlow, H. F., and Zimmermann, R. R. "Affectional Responses in the Infant Monkey." *Science* 130 : 421–432, August 21, 1959.

Harris, G. W., and Michael, R. P. "The Activation of

Sexual Behavior by Hypothalamic Implants of Oestrogen." *The Journal of Physiology* 171 : 275–301, 1964.

Heersema, P. H. "Homosexuality and the Physician." *The Journal of the American Medical Association* 193 : 815, September 6, 1965.

Leach, E. "Ourselves and Others." *The Listener,* November 30, 1967, p. 693.

Leach, E. "Men and Morality." *The Listener,* December 7, 1967, p. 749.

Lehrman, D. S. "The Reproductive Behavior of Ring Doves." *Scientific American* 211 : 48–54, November 1964.

Levine, S. "Sex Differences in the Brain." *Scientific American* 214 : 84–90, April 1966.

Sternberg, D. "Sweden Debates Sex Morality." *American-Scandinavian Review,* Spring 1966, p. 37.

Thorpe, W. H. *Learning and Instinct in Animals.* Cambridge, Mass., Harvard University Press, 1963.

CHAPTER EIGHT

Billingham, R. E. "Tissue Transplantation: Scope and Prospect." *Science* 153 : 266–270, July 15, 1966.

Burgess, A. M., Jr., Colton, T., and Peterson, O. L. "Categorical Programs for Heart Disease, Cancer and Stroke. Lessons from International Death-Rate Comparisons." *New England Journal of Medicine* 273 : 533–537, September 2, 1965.

Crile, G., Jr. *Cancer and Common Sense.* New York, Viking Press, 1955.

Crile, G., Jr. *A Biological Consideration of Treatment of Breast Cancer.* Springfield, Illinois, Charles C. Thomas, 1967.

Lecky, W. E. H. *History of European Morals.* New York, George Braziller, 1955.

Page, I. H. "An 'Uncommoner' Report on Conduct of Research." Editorial in *Modern Medicine*, September 27, 1965, pp. 127–130.

U.S. Department of Commerce, Bureau of the Census. "Statistical Abstract of United States, 1941." 63rd number. Washington, D.C., U.S. Government Printing Office, 1942.

CHAPTER NINE

Allen, D. L., and Mech, L. D. "Wolves Versus Moose on Isle Royale." *National Geographic* 123 : 200–219, February 1963.

Carrighar, S. "Ethologists." *The New York Times Magazine,* September 16, 1967, p. 14.

Crile, G. *A Mechanistic View of War and Peace.* New York, The Macmillan Company, 1915.

Davis, K. "Population." *Scientific American* 209 : 63–71, September 1963.

Harrison, D. Ref. 105, "The Control of Cell Division: *A Review* II. Special Mechanisms," by M. M. Swann. *Cancer Research* 18 : 1118, November 1958.

Hediger, H. Quoted by Hall, E. T. "Territorial Needs and Limits." *Natural History*, December 1965.

Ingle, D. J. "Racial Differences and the Future." *Science* 146 : 375, October 16, 1964.

Kalckar, H. M. "Galactose Metabolism and Cell 'Sociology.'" *Science* 150 : 305–313, October 15, 1965.

Larson, A. "Can Science Prevent War?" *Saturday Review,* February 20, 1965, p. 15.

Leach, E. "Men and Learning." *The Listener*, December 14, 1967, p. 780.

Lecky, W. E. H. *History of European Morals.* New York, George Braziller, 1955.

Lorenz, K. *King Solomon's Ring.* New York, Thomas Crowell Company, 1952.

Lorenz, K. *On Aggression.* New York, Harcourt, Brace & World, 1966.

Maeterlinck, M. *The Life of the White Ant.* London, G. Allen and Unwin, Ltd., 1927.

Marais, E. *The Soul of the White Ant.* New York, Dodd, Mead and Co., 1937; Introduction, by Dr. Winifred de Kok, quoted by Robert Ardrey in *African Genesis.* New York, Atheneum, 1961.

Mead, M. Quoted in *Science News* 92 : 583, December 16, 1967.

Medawar, P. B. *The Uniqueness of the Individual.* New York, Basic Books, Inc., 1957.

Milgram, S. "Behavioral Study of Obedience." *Journal of Abnormal and Social Psychology* 67 : 371–378, October 1963.

"Peking Urges Birth Curbs; Big Families Are Penalized." *The New York Times,* April 27, 1966, p. 1.

Rick, C. M., and Bowman, R. I. "Galapagos Tomatoes and Tortoises." *Evolution* 15 : 407, December 1961.

Russell, W. M. S. "The Affluent Crowd." *The Listener,* November 12, 1964.

Wigglesworth, V. B. *Life of Insects.* Cleveland, The World Publishing Company, 1964.

Wynne-Edwards, V. C. "Self-Regulating Systems in Populations of Animals." *Science* 147 : 1543–1548, March 26, 1965.

CHAPTER TEN

Bridgman, P. W. *The Way Things Are.* Cambridge, Mass., Harvard University Press, 1959.

Bulfinch, T. *The Age of Fable.* Philadelphia, David McKay, 1898.

INDEX

ABOUT THE AUTHOR

Dr. George Crile, Jr., who graduated *summa cum laude* from the Harvard Medical School in 1933, has been a member of the surgical staff of the Cleveland Clinic since 1937. He has served as the head of the Department of General Surgery since 1956.

Dr. Crile has published more than 300 scientific articles in professional journals. His previous books include *More Than Booty, Practical Aspects of Thyroid Disease,* and *Cancer and Common Sense.* Dr. Crile has made important contributions to the fields of cancer research (where he continues to challenge prevalent ideas concerning certain types of cancer operations) and marine archeology (he found a previously undiscovered Minoan city).

Dr. Crile and his wife, Helga, the daughter of Carl Sandburg, live in Cleveland Heights.